THE

UNRELIABLE
NATURE WRITER

Claire Carroll

First published in 2024
by Scratch Books Ltd
London

Jacket design © Alice Haworth-Booth, 2024
Typesetting by Will Dady
Printed and bound on carbon-balanced paper
in the UK by CMP Books

ISBN 978-1-7398301-8-2

Contents

THE
UNRELIABLE
NATURE WRITER

The Unreliable Nature Writer
Waits Outside The Church With Some
Of The Other Guests

– Hello.

Hi.

– That's an interesting outfit.

Thanks.

– What are those, sort of like feathers or something?

Scales, actually.

– Oh right, they look like feathers, but yes I see that they're kind of…silky? Are they real?

No.

– Right, right. Of course not. So, how do you know them?

Who?

– Um. The couple? How do you know the couple?

I lived with them for a while.

– Oh wow, what? Both of them? I feel like we should have met before. Were you at their exhibition? I feel like I would have met you there. Would you like some of this confetti? Sorry, what was your—oh look, there they are in the doorway—Sorry, what were you—what do you do?

I'm an Unreliable Nature Writer.

– Oh, a nature writer! That's interesting. How long have you been doing that?

Sort of forever, really.

– OK. So, is that, like, a job?

A bit. I mean, I don't get paid for it or anything.

– Right. More of a vocation then.

I suppose you could say that.

– And—sorry, I didn't quite catch all of what you just said— did you say you were a certain type of nature writer?

Yes. An unreliable one.

– Oh—haha—right. What...what does that mean?

You don't know what the word 'unreliable' means?

– Oh well, yes. I do, of course I do. It means flaky, or untrustworthy, or inconsistent. Of course, I know that. It's just that it's quite an interesting statement to make about yourself. I'm not sure I've heard that one before. Do you mean 'unreliable' in the sense that you're not an 'expert', like, in the scientific sense? Is that it?

I'm not an expert, no.

– But don't you need to be an expert to write about nature?

I don't know.

– I'm sure your viewpoint can't be dismissed as untrustworthy *just* because you're not a qualified scientist.

Who said I wasn't a qualified scientist?

– You...you just did. Just now you said—

I don't know what you're talking about.

– You said, just now, that you weren't an expert.

Oh yes. Yes, that does sound like something I might say. Look, I think they're finishing the photographs, we should probably get ready. Is this the type of confetti made from lots of tiny dead flowers?

– Yes. Seems to be. It's quite popular nowadays I think, as a sustainable alternative—

Pretty morbid to throw dead flowers over our friends.

– Oh wow, yes. I hadn't thought of it that way.

It looks nice though.

– Yes, yes it does.

It goes with their colour scheme.

Dream Reading:
On Higher Ground

A reader enters a room. It's a hired meeting room in a former stately home, which is now used as a series of offices and meeting spaces. Small companies operate there, people hot-desk. The stately home is approached by an imposing driveway with lawns either side. There is a ginkgo tree and a pond on the right-hand side of the lawn. There is a cloud hedge to the left. The hired meeting room is already full of people who are talking quietly—a low hum—and taking seats around a blond pine-veneer table in the centre of the room. They are dressed smartly. They have name badges pinned to their lapels, but the lettering is so small that the reader can't make out any of their names. She walks over to the head of the table. All of the windows in the meeting room are open. It is the morning, but already very hot:

Claire dreamt that she was in her own house; one that she had bought with her own money. She dreamt that she was standing by the window in the bedroom of the house, looking out over a lake. It was a loch, actually, and it was early morning. It was summer, but summer mornings in Scotland are crisp and cold and so she had a shawl, made of thin

red wool, wrapped around her shoulders. The loch was dark
grey, and the water wrinkled in the breeze. On the other side
of it were brown hills, springy with heather.

The reader pauses. There is a jug of water on the table. She
takes the glass nearest to her and pours some in, drinks it.
Some of the people sitting at the table do the same. The
man nearest to her is very attractive. Everyone in the room
is incredibly, disturbingly, grotesquely attractive. He is
sweating excessively in the early morning heat. She can see
the dark patches creeping from under his arms, but it looks
good on him. He stares at her as she sips, and sips again. She
clears her throat:

He was there too, in the dream; asleep in the bed, on his
front, with his hair falling over the left side of his face, his
back rising and falling. Claire thought about waking him,
but then, she thought that maybe if she woke him, that she
would also wake herself, and that the dream would be over.
So instead she left him there, stretched out, with one arm
hanging over the edge of the mattress.

'Can I just—' says the sweating, attractive man.
    The reader looks up from her paperwork.
    'Can I just stop you there?' he says. Some of the other
people sitting around the table look pleased that the man has
just stopped her there.

12

'Great. Thanks. So, before we go any further, we should probably make sure all the documents are here, so that we can check them over. Angela, do you want to—yes—thanks.'

Angela, who has makeup applied so impeccably that her face appears to be in higher definition than those of all the others in the room, gets up out of her seat. The reader takes a plastic document wallet out of her bag and hands it to Angela.

'Thank you,' Angela says. The man with the sweat patches nods to the reader and leans back in his chair.

Claire dreamt that the front door of the house that she had bought with her own money was open, and that she should probably go downstairs and close it. There were woods at the back of the house, and Claire found herself there, the red shawl still wrapped around her shoulders. The ends of it trailed behind her, brushing over ferns that were curled up tight like babies' fists. It was quiet; almost silent. But when she looked up, she could see the clouds rushing overhead like a waterfall, air fizzing with biting insects. Claire could feel her feet in the wellingtons as she walked uphill. She remembered that this was still a dream, and that soon she would wake up.

'Babies' fists?'

'I like it.'

'Me too, quite strange though.'

'And that *he* there, in the bed. Who *is* he?'

'It's quite unusual yes, do we think we should make a note—'

'Angela, could you?'

Angela gets up again and moves next to the reader with her notebook. It's spiral-bound at the top, like an old-fashioned reporters' notebook. The reader can see that Angela is writing in shorthand. She can see that Angela, too, is sweating. Gleaming, even. Although her makeup stays perfectly in place.

'Angela, could you make sure you make a note about the fists? Good. And the *he*, obviously? Great. Thanks.'

There is a muttering, but the reader clears her throat and raises her voice slightly.

The woodland path took a turn uphill and the fir trees thinned out. Up there the sky was a milky blue. The fir trees were gone, and an orchard stretched out in every direction, all at once. The apple trees bent and curled in on themselves and grew larger as Claire moved through the orchard; the grass grew taller too. Drops of dew like glass eyes gazed at her as she walked past. The grass trailed like seaweed in the watery air and rolled out ahead for miles.

The reader becomes aware of two people who are sitting near the back of the room. Not at the central table, but on chairs that are placed against the wall, near the door. They are dressed smartly too, but in matching outfits, uniforms. One of these uniformed people is bald, and the other has short hair, vibrantly blond. They have their heads bowed towards each other. They appear to be whispering. The reader notices that the uniformed person with the blond hair is grasping the document wallet which was handed to Angela earlier. The reader stops, but the two uniformed people keep whispering. The others in the room don't notice. The reader inhales—deeply—through her nose and starts again.

There were apples nestled in the grass, russet-coloured and overripe. Claire stopped and crouched down to look at one of these too-large apples where it lay in a hollow of cool grass. It was warm when she touched it. It uncurled at her feet, and then wasn't an apple, but a fat brown bird with a long neck. The bird rolled onto its front, found its feet and bobbed away through the tall grass. Around her, more of these apple-birds uncurled across the floor of the orchard (whose trees now were huge, like cedars, rainforest trees, telegraph poles) and began hopping away.

'I'm just wondering,' says a woman sitting on the reader's right-hand side, 'whether we could have more of the birds?'

'Yes, I'd like more of the birds too,' says the sweating, handsome man. 'It'll make more sense with the paperwork if we have birds in it.'

The reader's mouth is dry. There *are* birds in it, of course there are birds in it, but this is so much more intensive than she had been told it would be. This is too much scrutiny, too much management. And too many people. The uniformed pair at the back have stopped whispering now, and are staring at her, nodding their heads to the murmurs of 'more birds' coming from around the table. The reader is hot. The sun is pouring through the sash windows. The reader takes three deep breaths, like she practised:

Claire wondered whether they were pheasants, or grouse, seeing as how this was Scotland. Scotland is a place to feel remote; detached. When she thought about it, Scotland was the only place for her to have this dream. Thinking too much about the reasons for the dream was a sign that Claire was waking up. She didn't want to do that, because she wanted to get back to her new house with the wooden floors and the old-fashioned bed where he was asleep on his front, or maybe awake now, making coffee, sitting down to read in the old armchair whose leather was split and warped. He could read a whole book while he waited for her. He did that sometimes, even in real life. In real life he was a fast reader and could remember books off by heart. He could pull the names of poems out of the air. He wouldn't mind waiting at all.

The reader pauses here, even though there isn't a natural break in the reading. She had expected at this point for there to be more questions from the room about who *he* is. But no one seems interested in that anymore. This is her specialty, she supposes, this is what they've been expecting from her. It feels too easy to have escaped further questions about anything else, but she's relieved to be able to move on. The reader considers herself an anxious person. She hates public speaking (her mouth gets so dry), and she hates feeling exposed. She hates this heat, she hates scrutiny. She hates being found out. *Reading your very best dreams out in front of the housing panel is not for the faint hearted!* the forums all said. *But, if successful, it's a great way to get your foot on the ladder!* The reader hates interviews, high-pressure conversations, probing questions. She hates writing down her dreams. She hates talking about her feelings. These situations make her sweat and pulsate intensely. And yet, she finds there is something quite uniquely thrilling about putting herself into these situations—where the stakes are high, where it all might come crashing down—and getting away unscathed. The group seems restless now, fidgety. The reader checks the clock on the wall.

Angela has stopped taking notes and is reading something on her device. Her long fingernail glides sideways across the screen. Every so often she smiles to herself. One of the uniformed pair at the back produces a small bag of boiled sweets and passes it round the table. The reader starts to panic, quietly, just on the inside, that she's losing their attention.

By now a carpet of birds stretched out across the forest floor, all running, all bobbing along like the rushing waters of a stream that had burst its banks and, before Claire realised what was happening, the birds had swept her up, tipped her onto her back and were carrying her along, their feathers tickling her bare arms, their little bodies slipping and rustling through the long grass. The orchard fell away as the tide of birds swept out onto the moorland, across the brown springy heather, skimming and rushing forth under the sky.

'Oh lovely, that's great, well thank you so much, I think we're just about at our time.'

'No, no, I don't think—'

'She's finished, isn't she?'

'No, she's still got a couple of minutes.'

'Yes, but we've heard enough.'

'Too much, even. I'm really unsure about a lot of what's being said here—'

'What about the birds? There wasn't nearly enough about the birds.'

'We've got enough to go on, though. Haven't we?'

'No, not at all, not nearly enough.'

The sweating man (who, by now, the reader has realised, is the Housing Liaison Manager—the one the forums had warned her about) is standing up. He begins pacing about the room. The sweat has spread across his back and has soaked his shirt. The moisture drips onto the floor as he moves. He pushes his damp hair away from his forehead. He takes the nearly empty bag of boiled sweets from the centre of the table and starts popping them, one by one, into his mouth. The reader checks the clock on the wall.

'Look,' the Housing Liaison Manager says to the reader, his words thickened by the sweets inside, 'there's no doubt that you're close to the threshold. There's no doubt about that. But we are nearly at the limit of our time and there's still more that needs to be done, do you understand? More that needs to *happen* here.'

Angela looks encouragingly at the reader, nods her head a few times—quickly—to indicate that she can continue. The reader starts up again, her voice feels higher in pitch, frantic to get through it all in the time.

They stopped on the shore; a stony beach. They were on the edge of the loch. Claire was on her feet again then, and the birds were all around her. Far away on the other side she could just make out the house—

'Clock's ticking!'

'We've really got to wrap this up, I think this is all we ca—'

'Shh no, let her finish.'

The group are all up out of their seats and have moved closer to the reader. They are all sweating. Everyone's meticulously applied makeup—even Angela's now—is starting to smudge and run down their smooth faces. The uniformed pair at the back are now standing in front of the door. The reader notices two other uniformed people, that she hadn't seen before, standing next to the open window. She can't see her document wallet anywhere. It's got her passport in it, and her driving licence, and all her bank statements. A uniformed person by the window reaches over and closes it, draws the venetian blinds. The room dims instantly.

She panicked, wanting to know if he was still there. What if he left? What if this part of the dream was almost finished? The birds stood together on the shore, tightly knit, their little beaks like arrows, gleaming in the sun. There was a wooden boat, attached to a rock with a blue painter. Claire ran her hand along the rope, it was dry and frayed. The boat had no oars, no motor. The birds stood and watched, each one of their hard, black eyes alight with reflections of the noon sun.

'Oh this is excellent!'

'Now we're really getting somewhere!'

'I'm fully invested now!'

The sweating man—the Housing Liaison Manager—has taken off his tie and undone three of his shirt buttons. His hair is slick and glistens in the thin shards of sunlight that are pushing through the cracks in the blinds. The group are all clumped around him now, eyes wide, faces alight with anticipation. Several of them are grasping each other's hands or rubbing each other's shoulders. The reader checks the clock on the wall. They're well over time now, but she keeps going.

Claire crouched down in front of the birds. Perhaps they could take her back to him before it was too late. She could get back there, surely; she must. She closed her eyes and willed the birds to sweep her up again, take her back to the house and jostle her upstairs and into the bed in the middle of the room and underneath the duvet, underneath one of his arms with her face pressed up against his, with his eyelashes touching her cheek —

'That's it! Yes!'

'Excellent, definitely over the threshold, well over.'

'Congratulations!'

Angela starts a round of applause and the blinds are opened again. The reader is presented with her document wallet, and a set of keys.

'Yes, congratulations!'

'How does it feel to finally be on the property ladder?'

'Yes, it must feel amazing! Does it?'

'You're one of just two percent of people who meet the threshold.'

'You should feel very proud of yourself!'

The reader takes the wallet and the keys. There's an address on the key fob, printed in tiny letters. She tries to read it, but the sweat has made her vision hazy. She hopes it's the one she wanted—with the small garden that overlooked the marine lake—but at this point she is too elated to care. Someone hands her a glass of champagne, they're all handing around glasses of champagne, and she drinks hers in three gulps. Her glass is refilled, and she drinks that one too. People are hugging each other, coming over to the reader, embracing her, shaking her hand too. It's hard to do when everyone is sweating so much; their hands sort of slither out of hers. The air is thick with bodily moisture and chatter. The reader takes off her jacket. Everyone has taken off their jackets and kicked off their shoes which are strewn under the table.

'Oh, hang on, I think she's just got a tiny bit more to—'

The reader doesn't hesitate; she opens her mouth, beaming widely:

Instead, the mechanical trill of a blackbird washed in, just then, on a grey ache of daylight, making her eyes water and forcing them open—

An alarm sounds, a high-pitched, bawling noise that rattles the windows, lances eardrums. The group are startled, and some laugh, although some members look frightened—the sound is awfully, painfully loud—and start grabbing at their discarded shoes and bags and jackets, scurrying around the room, bashing into each other. The attractive, sweating boss raises his voice and tells everyone to calm down, but no one hears him. They try the door, but it's locked from the outside. Some of the people start to hyperventilate. Angela is hyperventilating. She's made to sit on a chair with her head between her knees as the alarm wails on. The uniformed person by the window hurries to open it, and the group—as one—peer over the window ledge. The meeting room is only one floor up, and beneath is a thick bed of lavender. It's in full flower, heaving with bees and butterflies. The Housing Liaison Manager pokes his head out of the window and makes a quick calculation. Then, he indicates to the others to watch what he's doing. He lowers himself onto the window ledge, hesitates only slightly, before dropping into the lavender below. The group follow his lead, one by one, the alarm shrieking with ever-increasing volume, exiting via the open window and dropping onto the vegetation. The reader is helped up onto the ledge by the bald uniformed person. It's too high, she thinks, looking at the mess of purple flowers below. Her hay fever is already making her face hum. The room behind her feels hot, and she can smell something besides the lavender, something like singed hair and burning plastic, like when an old radiator is turned on after a long time. The reader climbs into the aperture and swings her legs over the window ledge, and they dangle for a moment. As she drops, she squeezes her hands tight around the document wallet and the keys. Their metal ridges dig into the skin of her palm. She lands, and the world clunks sideways—the blue sky swooping upside down for a moment—and then upright again. The woody stalks of the lavender scratch her legs quite badly, and several bees sting her on the face and hands. Some of the others are worse off: Angela, who went out just before her, has a bleeding gash on her head and looks like she's sprained her ankle, but is laughing with what looks like relief, sprawled half in and half out of the flower bed.

The sun is too hot. It's far, far too hot to be outside, but the reader has her documents and her keys, and has reached the threshold, so really, everything is pretty great. The attractive Housing Liaison Manager is already halfway down the driveway, jogging backwards, his shirt unbuttoned, his trousers torn at the knees. He is shouting instructions to the others who are skipping and laughing along quite happily now in the blistering sunshine as a wide column of thrashing, bluish smoke floods upwards from the stately home's roof.

Quarterhorse

He's the last of his kind. Very special. Hundreds of years of breeding. Look at his legs! See how he's exceptionally muscular. He's a direct descendant of the Godolphin Arabian. You know what that means, son? An unbroken lineage. Purity.

The boy can see his reflection in the glass of the enclosure, and beyond that, in the animal's dark eyes. He can see the man standing behind him, with the carry case between them on the ground. It's early, there are no other visitors here yet. It's warm, but there are leaden clouds that hang low in the air. The man checks the weather on his device.

That was in England. When they got them here, way back in the beginning, they got them to breed with the ones that the Spanish brought over. It improved them, made them strong and fast; beautiful. These animals could do all kinds of things. They could run at breakneck speeds, carry stuff, even—and this is great—they could even be trained to do these little dances to music. Imagine! Those powerful hooves doing dainty, precise steps, and all with a human being on their back. His ancestors saw it all.

The boy doesn't move. The man sighs, wonders if the boy is fully engaged. It's early, but then they have a lot to get through today.

You learned about the conquistadors, right? You know about them. Do you think it's strange to think about that now? I did when I was your age, my god. All those centuries of invasion and colonisation. All that blood spilled. No one knew any better. All of us are still learning. Even me…

The animal moves deftly towards them. Dips its muscular head. Exhales. The boy stiffens; his limbs straighten. The man puts his hand on the boy's shoulder.

Oh, don't worry about him. He'll do that, but he's perfectly safe. We're perfectly safe too. Us out here, with him in there. Where was I? Yes. The learning, or rather unlearning. We'll never be free of it, not really.

The animal is very close. The boy reaches for the man's hand. The man pats it but doesn't take it in his. The boy needs to learn about these things.

Son, you're twelve now, is that right? So that means you've been through the programs that they insist upon for your age group. It was a malignant world for a long time. But we fixed a great deal of the turmoil, not long before you came along.

What do you think of that? What do you think of your luck, to be around now, after it was all fixed?

The boy doesn't reply, but the man sees his eyes widen slightly in the reflection of the glass. A good sign. The animal whickers and, with its teeth, wrestles hay from the net that hangs in the corner of its enclosure. The boy stares at the animal's brawny legs. They are a deep reddish-brown. They seem impossibly smooth for those of a live animal. The tail quivers.

You're wondering about his skin, aren't you? A lot of people wonder about that. It is real. I know; it looks like a simulation, right? But I can assure you it's genuine. We only have what God gave us, but this is the real deal; the archetype against which everything else is a copy. If you've seen those 4D zebras, then you'll be able to compare them to this guy. The detail on those is fine I guess, but up close you can always tell. Zebras were a totally different species anyway.

The animal turns. There are other people here now, the boy can see their reflections swirling behind him in the glass. The other people are chattering, crowding the exhibit; he can feel the heat of them as they gather at his back. He hears *Mom! Come look at this!* as a child in a backwards baseball cap pushes in front of him. The man stands his ground, keeping a firm grip on the boy's shoulder. The child in the backwards hat looks up at the boy and the man for a moment, and the man fixes it with a firm stare. The boy doesn't seem to notice.

Did you know that there's this island in Antarctica called South Georgia? It's a museum site now so only a limited number of people can visit each year, but hundreds of years ago it was the epicentre of the whaling industry. Can you imagine? Whales were a valuable commodity for a long time. They were filled with this substance—I forget what it's called now—but people would go out in huge ships that cut through the ocean. They would chase the whales over thousands of miles of water, spearing them; exhausting them. The blood would turn the water a dark blackish red. You've read Moby Dick, *right? Have you done that program yet? And you understand about the context? Context is everything.*

The boy feels tired. His eyelids grow heavy. It's the heat, or perhaps he has been standing still for too long. The exhibit is busy now, with families and children tearing around, pressing their faces up to the glass and mesh of the various enclosures. Someone says, *so muggy today!* and someone else says, *looks like rain!* He checks the weather on his device again.

This island—South Georgia—was where the biggest blue whale ever recorded was pulled out of the ocean. Pulled out and then cut up; its meat fed to small animals, its blubber

28

all rendered down and used for margarine, its bones—think about it, all of those bones, imagine the weight of them altogether!—used to make parasol pins and collar stiffeners and keepsakes and fripperies. Imagine walking around with a slice of whalebone in your shirt collar. They thought nothing of it back then. I know, it's just awful. Barbaric; shameful. Blue whales can live for over a hundred years. That one they pulled out could have been in the ocean for a century. I can't really think about this for too long, son. But we must confront it. One day I'll take you there, to South Georgia I mean. It'll be good for us; important for you.

The animal finishes eating and moves to the back of its enclosure, away from the child in the backwards cap who is rapping with its sweaty, sticky hand on the glass. The boy feels sick, like he's overheating. There's definitely moisture in the air, the man can feel it on his arms, but he presses on.

You probably wonder why I brought us to see this guy and then talk about whales. You're probably thinking we may as well have gone to look at the dinosaurs in the museum, right? But these big animals, these huge organisms, they're all so important. It's important that you learn about them all. They were so powerful. So beautiful, so majestic. But they were nothing without human intervention. The way we engineered them, all that interfering. Terrible. But nothing compared to everything else, you know? This guy's ancestors would have seen all kinds of awful things, all manner of terrible bloodshed, in the name of Acquisition. Do you do the program on Acquisition? Good, good. Humans were—by far—the very worst to each other.

The animal stares at the boy from the back of the enclosure. The boy doesn't move. The man can sense him thinking though—looking—trying to locate something; straining for a glimpse of something. Then, the animal's eyes grow wide, it bends deeply at its hind legs, pushes its front legs away from the floor, hooves stretching into the air. It flares its nostrils, bares its teeth. The boy bares his teeth too. *This is good*, the man thinks. *This is working*. The animal starts to make a noise, a long, low, moaning sound that seems to roll out of it in shuddering waves, through the metal, through the fortified glass of the enclosure, through the earth. The boy opens his mouth wide and draws his shoulders up to his ears. The man is encouraged by this. The boy sucks air into his mouth, starts to shake, and emits his own noise; different to that of the animal, higher in pitch. The other visitors look over. The animal's eyes are bright and lucid. The boy's face hangs open, his jaw locked. The man holds on to the boy's shoulders, both hands now, squeezes them. The boy stops. So does the animal. It retreats to the back of the enclosure, huffing through its nostrils. Ribbons of saliva drape from its mouth. The sweaty child in the backwards cap starts to cry, and its mother appears. She looks at the man, and then at the boy, and briskly pulls her sweaty child away. The man watches her hurrying off, glancing back over her shoulder at them, quickening her pace. The other visitors back away too. The sky darkens. There is definitely moisture in the air. The exhibit is surrounded by a thick silence. The man clears his throat.

There's a lot of cultural evidence to suggest that human beings knew about all this too, isn't that fascinating? They had everything they ever wanted in the end, but it kept getting bigger and more acquisitional. I use that word a lot, I know, but it's a good one for you to learn. There are files that have been found—data, images and so on—that suggest they knew it was happening, but they carried on anyway. But it's like the Neanderthals I guess; they were only as good as the next best thing. You OK, buddy?

The boy's eyes close. The man shakes the boy's shoulder gently, but the boy's head tips forward. It starts to rain. Fine, sour needles. The man sighs. Then, he picks up the boy and dismantles him; packs him away into the carrycase. The boy has made a degree of progress today, the man reasons. It's important to acknowledge that this type of work isn't usually carried out in such unorthodox ways. But convention and tradition are overrated. He picks up the carrycase and takes a last look at the animal, who has started to pace around the inside edge of its enclosure, its feet moving with dainty, precise steps.

Infinite Husbands

I'll let you in on a little secret: I have a lot of husbands. I don't have time to tell you about all of them, but we could talk about some—maybe ten—unless I get tired and then I'll stop telling you about them. Please don't be under any illusion that these are the most important husbands, or the most recent, and please don't ask me any questions about how I maintain a life with so many husbands; that's none of your business.

My first husband is handsome but quick to emotion. When I first met him, he cried a lot about how his mother had abandoned him as a child. She ran off with a swimming instructor and was never seen again. His father couldn't cope. As a result, my first husband was very needy, but I looked after him. I gave him what he needed—gave him what he hadn't had from his mother—and in time he became less needy. We don't see each other very often nowadays, but he knows I love him.

My second husband is hilarious and cruel and devastatingly handsome, with watery blue eyes. He is so handsome that I can't even think about him for too long as my heartrate rises unbearably, and I have to lie down. He has been missing for quite some time.

My third husband looks exactly like me in every way, to the point where we are often mistaken for the same person. He likes me to cut my hair very short, to match his. This can upset the other husbands, but not one of them is brave enough to fight husband number three over it. He is prone to aggressive outbursts. Once we were in a pub having Sunday lunch, when a man at the next table bumped into husband number three, spilling some of his drink onto our table. Before I knew what was happening, husband number three had jumped up and flung his own drink, glass and all, into the man's face. The man screamed and my husband roared back at him. My husband was eventually dragged from the pub by two police officers, his shirt ripped and covered in the man's blood. I bought him that shirt, it was a Paul Smith one.

My fourth and fifth husbands are twins, two sides of the same coin. They are musicians in a band together, one plays the drums and the other sings. Now, I know what you're thinking, and you can stop right there. It's not at all like that. They hate being fetishised in that way. They are very sweet boys; sweet men. Beautiful mirror images. I prefer one over the other, but I would never tell them which, or you, so you can stop asking.

My sixth husband is very elusive but is, by far, one of the most intelligent men I have ever met. He lives near the sea. It's a long journey but I visit whenever I can. He works as a scientist, monitoring the ocean for pollution levels. The house he lives in dates from the early twentieth century and is an excellent example of the art-deco style, with huge windows that look out over the beach. The light inside the house is exquisite; the sun bounces off the sea and reflects on the walls and ceilings. He favours minimalism; doesn't keep much in his house. He's very precise, this husband. Neat and orderly. He likes that I am not like this; he likes that I am artistic, messy, even chaotic at times. He likes to think he can smooth my rough edges with his clean, scientific precision. I love staying with him. We walk along the beach in the wind, watching oystercatchers skittering in and out of the little waves that break on the foreshore. Sometimes, on a clear day, you can see pilot whales, far out to sea. My sixth husband doesn't like me to stay for long, but he likes for us to be in almost constant contact. He gave me this device. Here it is, see? No, it's not a mobile phone; I think it's some sort of tracker. Something they use a lot in oceanography.

Can you see the garden any better now that the sun is coming out? Those tulips over there look nice in the light, don't they? We planted them all when we moved here. I say *we*, but it was all me. It took a long time but it's worth it. Yes, they really are that huge, and nearly impossible to grow. They're quite rare too. Take a good look. They'll be gone soon.

My seventh husband is vicious and manipulative. If he shows up while you're here you should hide or — better still — slip out the French windows into the garden. I'll distract him. No, honestly, don't worry. I'm not expecting him for hours. My eighth husband is much nicer; more dependable and much older than me. He has white hair that springs back from his forehead. He's very serious, but wise and calm too. We walk for hours together over fields and woodland. He likes to talk about philosophy. My mind wanders as he talks; I let his voice wash over me like music as we move through slices of evening sunshine. He's had the same pair of shoes for thirty years. No, he doesn't live here. They don't all live here with me. That would be absurd.

I met my ninth husband last year. He's tall and drinks heavily. He's the sort of person who wears novelty clothes all the time; a sweatshirt made of neon faux fur, brightly coloured trainers, slogan t-shirts. When I first met him, he was dancing wildly at a party. He noticed me and pulled me towards him. This husband smiles and jokes all the time, even when he's sober. He's a clown; a loveable fool. Most women don't look at him twice, not because he is unattractive, but because he is loud, drunk, ridiculous, prone to clumsiness. But that's what I like most about him. He calls me *princess,* but he does it ironically. We laugh so hard that we cry sometimes. Once he got really drunk and high and he overheated and had a seizure on the dancefloor of a nightclub. I went with him to hospital. The ambulance screeched through the cool morning air as dawn broke over the city. He cried like a baby when he regained consciousness; promised me he'd never scare me like that again.

I need a rest now, a glass of water or something. Do you need anything? Let's open the windows and let the air in at least. Why don't you go out there and take a look at those tulips? Honestly, this is your last chance. The company doing the digitising says it'll look exactly the same, but I'll know. Just go out there for five minutes and have a proper look. Take a picture of them; you won't regret it.

I didn't expect to meet my tenth husband so soon after the incident with my ninth. I had thought that perhaps I should slow down a little, take stock. But love finds you sometimes, doesn't it? It creeps up on you when you least expect it. Sometimes you're just walking along minding your own business, or else looking out of the window on the train, and it comes at you, fluttering past you on the breeze. There's nothing you can do if love finds you; you just have to give in, let the current pull you under. No, that's not how I've met all my husbands. Many of them I've pursued, courted, researched, even stalked if I've had to. I'm not passive about finding them, but sometimes you have to give in to love if it comes hurtling towards you.

My tenth husband is delicate; sensitive. He's not as tall or as handsome as some of my other husbands, but there's something in the curve of his cheekbones, the way he smiles; radiantly but self-consciously. We met on the way to a conference. He sat next to me on the train. It was an ultrafast one—you know, with a glass roof—and the sky sped past above our heads as we talked. We got drinks, realised we liked the same music. It felt easy; natural. He glanced out of the window and mentioned his significant other very quickly, as if he didn't really want me to hear. He wasn't wearing a ring, I noticed, but people don't nowadays do they?

When we arrived at the hotel where the conference was being held, we walked in together as though we were a couple. Instinctively we both reached out for the other's hand but let go quickly—laughing—eyes sparkling. The hotel was a vast expanse of white, like a ship, with the flat blue sky behind it. Our rooms were on different floors, but he knocked on my door before dinner that first night. We were dressed formally, for work, but I had put on perfume and lipstick. We walked past a wide mirror in the hotel lobby and I had to catch my breath when I saw our reflections. I could tell he did too.

Have you ever been in love? Yes, alright, but have you ever fallen in love without meaning to? And have you ever loved more than one person at once? Have you ever loved a great many people, an infinite number, all at the same time? Well, I suppose not, no. Otherwise you wouldn't be here, asking me all these questions.

I can't talk that much more about husband number ten. We need to be careful, or his *significant other* will find out. It would hurt my husband deeply if his *significant other* knew about me, and I can't bear the thought of him in pain. For this reason, we can't speak in person very often, but he leaves me messages—signs—to let me know he's thinking of me. Just the usual, you know. Squiggles on walls, soft melodies, cloud formations, tea-leaves. Things like that. It's kindest that way. I do think about his *significant other* from time to time. I'm not a monster. I'm not. I know what the *significant other* looks like (very beautiful, I'll admit) and I picture them sometimes, lying in bed next to one another as my husband sleeps peacefully. I imagine the *significant other's* eyes, wide open in the dark, tears pooling in the corners.

Husband twenty-one is broad and confident, with a kind smile. He plays basketball professionally. He has boundless energy, smooth skin, strong shoulders, long, dark eyelashes. I watch him sleeping sometimes, and I stay as quiet as possible, holding my breath so he doesn't wake up. Husband one-hundred-and-forty-eight is vast, as wide as he is tall, with rolls of pale double chins. He is exceptionally good at maths and can solve riddles better than anyone I know. He's an absolute riot at parties. There's another—I forget which number now—who has long limbs; he looks like a daddy-long-legs. He can juggle and ride a unicycle at the same time. He has an unpredictable streak—something erratic and undiscoverable—under all that jollity though; stay away from him if you can.

I haven't seen husband eighty-six for years, but we are connected by a thin silver thread. It's almost invisible and many miles long. I miss him, but it's comforting to know that he's there, at the end of that thread, and I could heave and pull him to me if ever I needed him.

There are more I could tell you about; I could go on for hours and hours. I can see them all now if I shut my eyes; all lined up neatly like binary code, stretching out forever. Imagine any husband and he has been mine, or is mine, or will be.

No, it's fine, I'm not tired. I can see that the light's going though, is it? Or is that just me? I'll continue. You don't mind, do you? This is the last of these gardens; everything will be in the cloud soon. Are you listening? I was just saying that it'll *all be gone soon*. Gone and not gone, or whatever. It's hard to know anymore what's there and what's not there, isn't it? I suppose you're used to it. You've never known any better.

The Sheer Delight of What
You May Become

Close your eyes. It's a lovely day, isn't it? We are going to imagine, together, a better world. We are going to picture the spores in the air. We are going to picture the trees as they exhale. We are going to choose a word to say, over and over. Green, green, green. We are going to imagine rivers flashing with life, slippery things that blaze with clarity. A fluttering here, bright eyes. Leaf glow. The overstory stretches up and out, the sky wheels on forever.

*

Phase One: Identification

Start by identifying an area of land within the designated juris-diction. This type of farmland is easy to spot on the main area maps. From these you can derive—using the land registry—the identities of the owners. The owners are desperate to sell. They are tied into a system of repayments due to the collectivisation that took place in the last century. Inflation made things untenable. You may already know this. You may have opinions on this. Opinions can be discussed afterwards.

Our first example of successfully identified Acquisition is illustrated here. Unit 2B is a 30-hectare area located in some lowlands. The soil was marshy, but the tenants—in this case—had managed, over the generations, to maintain cattle who thrived in these conditions. The meat from the animals raised on this land is considered a delicacy; a unique salty flavour. They supplied fine-dining establishments across the country and are exported internationally, predominantly to the United States, France and the Far East. It's difficult to imagine now; the excess of it all. That's not why we're here. After the livestock sanctions, the tenant family tried to continue within the confines of the permissible local supply chains, but these were not lucrative. Much of the land went into a wasted, depleted state, which was ideal for us when identifying property for Acquisition.

Important tips for Identification:

- Look for areas within neglected jurisdictions. Smallholdings and pastures that are in areas of low economic value will be easier to identify and eventually procure.

- Research the tenants as you identify the land. Look for those that are struggling. You may want to look at the condition of the barn roof, or assess the farm machinery as a key indicator of feasibility. Look for patchy grass, look for low annual yields.

- Try to be as dispassionate about the animals as you can. This is a challenge, even for the emotionally resilient, but bear in mind: the end result always justifies the means.

*

A woman and her brother sit at the kitchen table. It's still light outside, but the woman's child is upstairs in bed. It has been raining for eight days. The woman is sorting through a box of photographs that had belonged to their mother.

Where was this, she says, holding one up.

Disneyworld, Florida, says her brother.

We never went, I don't think?

Margate, then. I dunno.

Disneyland Margate?

He is peeling potatoes, placing them in a large pot full of cold water that sits next to him. The woman examines the outfits he and her brother are wearing in the picture. Neon-coloured cycling shorts, trainers laced up too tight. They are smiling, squinting into the sun, standing in front of the plastic form of Mickey Mouse. The woman puts the photograph away. She sorts through them most evenings, looking for something. She doesn't know what. She puts the box away on the side table, notices for the tenth time that day that the stack of unopened envelopes has grown. The clock on the wall ticks, out of step with a dripping tap.

*

The sun pushes through gaps in the clouds, and we feel the warmth bloom across the skin on our arms. We can smell the meadowsweet. Can we smell the meadowsweet? Can we hear that sound? It's the herd in the distance, there are bells around the cows' necks. They are moving through the pasture, through the valley, beneath the trees. Does it remind us of that holiday we took in the countryside that year? The sounds from the windchime that hung in the garden would merge with the cow bells. Maybe we don't; maybe it's too far away for the ear to grasp.

*

Phase Two: Acquisition

After Identification is complete, the State, and the tenants, will be notified of your intentions. The process of Acquisition should then be perfectly straightforward if you have followed the guidance above.

It is important to be aware of a number of challenges you may face during the Acquisition phase. The tenants will be relocated by the State to new residences. As the land is not theirs, they will vacate it directly. The State provides adequate housing. Despite unrest amongst tenant communities and activist groups, there is no need for acquisitors to be concerned; State housing is in the form of large, off-ground condominiums, with in-built Smart technology and temperature control. After an adjustment period, 85% of tenants were satisfied with their move which is important to bear in mind when starting the paperwork, although it is also important to ensure that the Acquisition advances in a timely manner. An Acquisition template is available to download covering the administrative, physical, interpersonal, and psycho-social elements of the process for both tenant and acquirer. In case of query or concern, you may wish to pass on the following assurance to any outgoing tenants:

- All human tenants from acquired farms and smallholdings will be accommodated in locations according to a tiered system of Needs Assessment.
- Housing locations will have at least the minimum square footage requirements, in adherence with the current legal framework.
- Locations will include fresh water supply, appropriate heating and cooling systems, natural daylight in all communal living spaces.
- Food supplies will be guaranteed in allotted dwellings for a minimum of two years post-relocation date.

*

The woman's brother is busying himself next to the stove, making supper, humming to himself. He heats oil in a heavy casserole dish. He's cutting onions and carrots as finely as he can with a blunt knife. The tune he is humming is 'Wake Me Up Before You Go-Go'. The woman thinks about offering to help, but it's better if they carry out their own tasks, busy themselves in their own individual ways. Besides, he was always better at cooking than she was. The stack of envelopes looms at her from the side table.

It won't hurt just to look, says her brother slinging a tea towel over his shoulder and reaching for a colander from the high shelf above the stove.

What's the point, though?

You'll feel better about it if you know what they look like.

Did you?

Not really. But you know how I am about the idea of feeling better.

The woman picks up an envelope from the pile on the side table, opens it up in the pale flickering of the overhead strip light. Inside, a brochure describes an apartment block. A headland, a beach. It's far away but looks lovely enough. There are codes to scan. She takes her device from her pocket. The codes take her to a simulated cliff path, flies her through a series of tall white buildings, all of them bright in the sunshine. Windows shimmer, reflecting a pale blue sky. People greet each other on paths between the dwellings, a woman pushes a baby in a pram, children run through a psychedelic wildflower meadow. At the centre, a lake, crystal-clear, teeming with fish. A child and its mother set sail to a paper boat from the shallows and the child claps its hands and laughs. Workers file out in streams, disappearing into a fine mist at the edges of the simulation.

It doesn't look too bad, the woman says, *the air seems clean enough.*

Not too bad, no, her brother nods, *and look, nice green areas, and a school that's good. Everything within a twenty minute walk.*

She won't like it.

No. But she'll get used to it.

*

Let's lie back in the grass. See it rise on all sides. Notice how each blade of grass has a ridge down its centre. We could spend a lot of time doing that here, we hear a skylark overhead. There's that dog barking again; children laughing in the distance. Move the backs of our hands, this way and that, through the grass. Let the collection of pointed blades embrace us. Then push down into the earth. Let us press with our fingertips until the soil resists beneath them. Let us keep pressing. The earth will be forced, slowly, through the gaps in our fingers, driven underneath our fingernails and stay there for days. Our fingers may collide with stones. When we drag our hands out and hold them up to the light, there will be the remnants of living creatures on their outer edges. Above us now, the sky is perfectly blue, and the sun, the sun—

*

46

Phase Three: Moving On

Some acquirers can find Moving On uncomfortable. Rest assured the majority of tenants will be delighted to be taking all of their furniture, kitchenware, clothing and mementos away in the boxes and removal vans that we provide; setting them out neatly and carefully in their new homes. However, with those *Dissatisfied* or *Very Dissatisfied,* you may hear phrases from the tenants such as *please reconsider* or *you have no right to do this* or *we have been here for generations* or *stop doing that to him, there's no need, you're hurting him.* Try your best to tune this out; you might remind yourself, and the tenants of the bright future ahead of us all, as a result of this mutually beneficial arrangement. The videos we provide are there to support you—

You are going to choose a word to say, over and over. Green. Green. Green. You are going to imagine rivers flashing with life, slippery things that blaze with clarity. You take the sound into our bodies and allow it to take root in our chests. You allow the sound and the vibration to fill our lungs—

We advise organising a series of therapy sessions around the time of Acquisition if you feel that this is necessary. However, there are ways in which the process can be made to run as smoothly as possible. Keep some stock phrases to hand. For example:

- 'We are looking forward to taking on this land and continuing to use it in the best possible way.'
- 'You have done a fantastic job of caring for this pasture, and we are honoured that you have chosen us to acquire it from you at this time.'
- 'Your stressors and overheads will be shrunk substantially.'
- 'The negotiation phase of this process has now passed its deadline.'

*

Dusk falls, and the sun swells fiercer, before dwindling behind the trees. The soil on our skin has dried into the cracks, the sky above hums purple. We start to hear the earth hum too, quietly at first, a low drone. The featherwing beetles, the small stones, the thin roots of the weeds that coil quietly. This sound, too, we take into our bodies, allowing it to take root in our chests. We allow the sound and the vibration to fill our lungs. We allow the sound and the vibration to fill our mouths. We allow the sound and the vibration to fill our bodies, entire. We find ourselves rising in the cool dark of the evening, and are together, on our feet, singing.

*

Phase Five: Livestock Management and
Structural Clearance

There is a high possibility that some livestock will remain after you have cleared the tenants. Depending on the district you have chosen to acquire, many will have been slaughtered by the tenants themselves prior to their Moving On. It is worth noting that most Acquirers find this to be the most emotionally burdensome part of the process. The choice to either rewild or destroy is not an easy one, especially if the Acquisitor role is new to you. For destruction, there are a number of agencies who will be able to help, and they will quote based on the retail value of the flesh yield, although do bear in mind that this is currently set at a high taxable rate.

Rewilding must be carried out by the new occupiers. Livestock must be herded away from the dwelling and into common pastureland. They must be de-tagged—traditional metal tags must be prised from the ears, or the more modern tagging system (retina implants) can be removed safely with a blade—and de-linked from the farm's system, which will in turn disable their linkages to the national system. In this pack you will find the device needed to de-tag them. It doesn't cause any lasting pain for the animal. Try not to look into its eyes when you do it.

Structural clearance may commence as soon as the livestock are removed from the premises. Burning is the only way in which this is possible. Your acquisitor pack will contain the incendiary materials necessary for a clean burn. It is vital to attend to every room on the property that you have acquired, to ensure that everything is fully covered in the flammable liquid before you ignite. Remember that some materials take to the burn more than others. It is not necessary to remove any of the loose items— sofas, beds, cutlery, artworks, clothing, photograph albums, etc— from the property before burning. The previous tenants will have taken everything permitted with them.

You may use the delayed ignition feature when you have withdrawn to a safe distance. We recommend a minimum of half a mile. We recommend staying inside your vehicle. The burn can take between twelve and twenty-four hours. When the flames have reduced to embers, you can return for cleansing and reseeding. Use the six bottles of hydrogen peroxide in your acquisitor pack. There are slow-release wildflower seed bombs which can be sown directly after the burned matter has been cleared.

*

The door to the cowshed is slick with rain. Inside, the three animals—the remains of the herd—give off a mist of collective thought. The woman makes her way over to them, runs her hand across the shoulder of the nearest cow. It moves towards her, then away, dips its head. There is no more dry feed in the troughs. The woman assesses which of the animals is the skinniest. The woman's daughter appears at her side, takes hold of her hand, placing the handle of a knife into her palm.

Can you count how many, baby?

I see three.

How many will there be tomorrow?

Only two?

Are you sure?

More than three?

That's right.

The woman looks down at her daughter's soft head. Patches of scalp are visible through strings of pale hair. She notices that the child's breathing is quieter this morning, less laboured than it has been in recent weeks.

I heard you talking at night time, she says, looking up at the woman.

Oh, what about?

When are they coming?

Tomorrow maybe.

That's soon.

Or the next day.

The cows shuffle back and forth. Their eyes are dull in the thickening light. The woman thinks about energy, about calories. In and out, fuel and fire. The child is sinewy and strong. The woman takes her knife and moves towards the thinnest cow. She strokes between its ears. When it falls to the floor it makes a sound like a felled tree.

*

We move. Slowly at first. The sound that rises from the earth moves us. Pushes and pulls us around and around and around in the dark. We rotate, hands together, as the stars sharpen above. We have done this, altogether. We are joined. Our feet peel away from the earth, lifting into the clear air of the night. The moon leaks through the branches in the distance. What is thought? Our sensations blur and drift. What about feeling? Roots break free, split open, form anew.

*

Phase Six: Ecstatic Regeneration

You will be able to see results from reseeding in as little as two weeks, depending on soil type. Once the shoots appear to be breaking the surface, you will be able to start releasing the invertebrates. Earthworms, slugs, flower beetles, yellow-jackets, dingy skippers, marmalade hoverflies, pantaloon bees, elephant hawkmoths. The grasses will grow tall, and field mice will start to appear. Then: bank voles, eurasian shrews, moles, dormice, mountain hares, red squirrels, pine marten, mink, polecats. You won't see all of these species straightaway, but as you plant the trees that will grow into copses and forests, and dig pits that will become ponds and pools, you will hear them. You will know that they are there.

Birds will come. Woodpeckers, starlings, swallows, herons, kites, storks. The ponds, along with the trenches you will dig to connect to our new waterway system, will be supplied with spawn. You will receive monitoring forms via your electronic device on a weekly basis. You will be required to fill in each form accurately. Checks are carried out on a monthly rotation. You may set up camp at the margins of the newly wilded zone, but must ensure that all your relevant documentation is at hand for when the onboarding team carry out their monitoring visits. Please refer to document 7A for a full list of terms and conditions relating to your tenancy on the newly acquired land, which includes details of next steps, once the regeneration process is complete. Enjoy it!

*

The woman and the girl work quickly to move the carcass. A fine rain has started to fall, so they don't drag it outside. Instead, they decide to work inside, even though the light isn't as good. The woman's brother appears in the entrance to the cowshed.

We don't have— her brother says.

We do. Days, at least three. It's enough—

To break this down, sure. But what then?

The woman sticks the knife into the cow's neck, and begins to cut around its circumference. Her brother feels his mouth fill with saliva.

You have no idea what you're doing, he says, his voice rising in pitch.

Just help.

The girl has gone to stand by her uncle. The two of them watch her remove the animal's head. She has to break its neck with her boot. The girl doesn't look away.

*

The herd is there, beneath our floating feet. Mist rises from their backs; a head turns here and there. Their eyes reflect our eyes, reflect the moon. They were always there. More of them join, or more of us. A grey light on the horizon. Time curls in on itself to a full stop. The rain falls, droplets rest on our skin, and wash onto the animal pelts. We rise and keep rising.

*

The woman wakes in a white room. It's early, but bars of yellowish light reach from behind the blinds and shoot across the ceiling, the sound of the sea in the distance. When she stretches, her feet touch the wall at the end of her bed. A double room, with space for a double bed. She hears the child turn in her sleep in the next room. The walls here are thin. She gets up, turns to the en-suite bathroom and washes her face. In the heated mirror, her face appears to her in high definition. In the kitchenette, the kettle has already started boiling for her cup of tea. The window offers an oblique view of the estate, which is shrouded in a fine grey mist. Over in the next block, she can see the windows of her brother's apartment. The lights are off. She opens the window, the air is damp and warm.

She drinks her tea. From the kitchenette, she can see the child sleeping in her bed. The child is lying on her side, breathing softly. The woman returns to her own room and reaches under the bed for the large storage box. When she breaks the seal from the lid, the smell of tallow and straw in the white cuboid room feels obscene. She unfolds a flat object. The hide wasn't tanned properly. They didn't have enough salt, or enough time. The child needed the clean air, the security. She takes the folded skin into the living areas. There are pieces of dried flesh still clinging to its underside. She spreads it, hair-side down across the floor of the open plan living space. It almost touches all four walls, even with the furniture pushed back. The woman sits in the centre, and, with her fingernails, sets about picking off the dried flesh. When she stands, she feels the softness of it under her bare feet. Outside, the sun rises, invisibly, behind the low-hanging mist.

The Unreliable Nature Writer
Finds Her Place And Sits Down For
The Wedding Breakfast

– Oh hello, it's you. It's the Unreliable Nature Writer. Is this
my name here? Looks like I'm next to you. Yes. Great. Are
you here by yourself then?

Sort of. Are you?

– Yes. I mean, no, I'm sitting here by myself. My wife is over
there with our kids. They were bridesmaids. The kids were,
I mean. You know, I was thinking about what you were saying
earlier, that stuff about being an Unreliable Nature Writer—

Were you.

– I was just thinking you needn't be so hard on yourself—
here, do you want some wine?—just because you're not a
scientist, it doesn't mean you can't write about nature.

A lot of double negatives there.

– Yeah, alright, but you know what I'm getting at.

I never said I can't write about nature.

– Didn't you? I thought —

I just said I was unreliable.

– Oh, right.

I can't be trusted. I'm not dependable —

– Shall we, erm. Oh look, the appetisers are here. This looks great, sharing plates — that's a popular choice these days, isn't it? Do you want me to...Oh, I'll just pass it to you?

Yes. I think that's best.

– It's funny how they call it a 'Wedding Breakfast' isn't it? Where does that come from, do you suppose?

I think it comes from the idea that the time after the wedding ceremony — like when the marriage has been completed, like contractually locked in, I mean — is a 'new day'.

– Oh right! Yes, that makes a lot of sense.

Or it could be that people fast to the point of starvation before their wedding ceremonies.

– What? Oh yes, haha. I suppose so. Um. So, writing. Interesting. What do you write about?

I write about the outdoors, mostly.

– Ah yes, well that's kind of what I thought.

I write about animals and plants.

– Right. OK. Yes.

And minerals and plastic and computers. And phones. And dreams.

– Wow. I had no idea nature writers did all that.

I'm not really a nature writer though.

– But you just said…we just talked about—

Yeah, but maybe I made that up.

– OK.

Maybe I just pretend to be a nature writer so that I have a reason to go and visit remote places. Maybe I use nature as a proxy to talk about myself. Maybe I'm just quite a selfish person who gets bored easily.

– Oh, wow. No, I'm sure that's not true—

Or maybe I'm not. Maybe I'm a genius. Maybe all my writing is the work of a genius.

– These are nice, aren't they? These little chicken skewer things—

I write a lot about dead birds.

– OK.

Dead birds are symbolic.

– Yes.

All dead animals are symbolic, really.

– Well, yes, I'm sure—

Although dead birds are interesting; in many cultures a dead bird is a symbol of new life.

– Is that so?

Yes. Although not here. Here a dead bird is just a dead bird.

– Right. A symbol of itself. That's a bit um—

Abject? Yes, probably. But kind of arresting. When we see a dead bird, like smeared across the road—sorry, yes I will have one of those skewer things—or curled up under a railway bridge or something, it makes us disgusted. But we can't look away.

– Are you talking about the sublime now?

The what?

– The idea of the sublime? I studied it a bit in my undergraduate degree. I did History of Art.

Oh right.

– You know about the sublime, surely—you must know.

No.

– But it's accepted theory, it's…it's a huge area of philosophy. Did you not read Kant at university?

Oh yeah. Sure.

– OK, so you know about this idea that the sublime is about being awestruck by nature—maybe a bit terrified of it— before realising its beauty.

Beauty is pretty meaningless, really.

– Um, yes. I suppose. Looks like they're clearing the platters over there already. Did you want any more of this one?

No thanks. Can you pass me the wine? Or just pour it in. That's it, all the way to the top. You may as well pour it all in, yeah. Thanks.

– You are quite defiant in your position as unreliable, aren't you?

It's important to acknowledge our limitations.

– Is it?

Yes. I would be lying if I said it was easy though.

– Is truth important?

Yes. Emotional truth, anyway. But even that is unreliable. Feelings pass, don't they.

– I suppose they do. What about climate change?

What do you mean?

– Do you have a position on it?

Yes.

– And what is that?

The correct one.

– Oh. Great. Yeah, me too.

Did you want to ask me anything else about nature writing?

– Oh, um. I think I can see my wife calling me over.

There Or Not There

Ok, fine. Fine. I'll tell you a true story. But this is the only one I've got. It's a horrible story though.

I was twenty-two, and I worked for a hybrid ethical advertising practice in Central London. I didn't know what I was doing there. I had no idea. The practice was commissioned, usually by the local authority or private companies, to deliver striking messages in public spaces. The practice was in a studio, located in a former warehouse, which had been damaged by a flood that summer (no, don't worry, that was before I started. That wasn't the thing I did). I was employed as a studio assistant to sort out all of the archived drawings and paperwork that had been damaged by the floodwater.

I was quite happy to re-file the crispy, dried-out papers. The work was better paid than the pub, plus I didn't have to work at night, or walk home with my phone and keys clenched in my hand, damp down my front from the drip trays, ears ringing. Working in the day was something normal adults did. So, if I did this type of proper work then I'd be a proper adult. London was full of this type of stratification.

Or maybe I was. I can see that now, OK? I can see that I was the one with the problem.

Perhaps because I seemed excessively happy to have been given this role, or perhaps because the directors had told them they should make use of me, the architects and architectural assistants started to ask me to help them on their projects.

Some people say that the structure of our practice veers towards anarcho-communism, one of the senior creatives said to me during my first week. I didn't understand what anarcho-communism was, but then I realised that he probably didn't expect me to. He went on to describe how the work they did was concept-driven, creatively led, no hierarchies within the staff, a horizontal network of collaborators, no company shareholders, no dividends.

It's about producing the best, most functional, most aesthetic and most meaningful design for the client, and for the public, he said. *Nothing else matters*.

I said something like, *oh, wow. Cool*.

Then he said: *it also means you don't have a boss, not really. Like, you're in charge of your own destiny here. No one is going to make you do anything you don't want to do*.

Years later, while working a temp job at another hybrid ethical advertising practice, whose directors all wore suits to work and underpaid their junior staff, I would remember that moment, and how I took it for granted.

Don't worry. It's not all like this. I'll get to the bad thing, I promise. It's coming.

I had been there three months when one of the junior creatives, Gael, asked me to help him on a project he was working on. Gael was five years older than me, serious, elegant and razor sharp. We ate lunch together in the park by the office. I guess you could say we became friends. The project was for a site that was in a patch of woodland on the far eastern edge of the city. Gael and I would take the tube east to visit the site, travelling to the end of the line, to where London wasn't really London at all anymore, but somewhere else; the countryside. Those parts of London-not-London are like a different world, somewhere that's between places; not really anywhere at all. I always wondered how people could just live there, going about their daily lives as if there was nothing weird about that.

Gael had designed a series of installations which would be placed throughout the woodland. These installations would replicate old-fashioned interior décor; bring things outside that should really have been inside. They would be fused with the natural surroundings, mostly in tree stumps or rocks or dead trees, and would form a trail through the woods that local residents could discover. There were codes to scan that gave you information about the client, but you could simply enjoy the trail without these. It would be charming and delightful and uncanny and interesting. At the centre of the trail was an ornate ladder that Gael had designed the year before. It looked like the type of ladder you'd find in an old-fashioned library—you know, the kind with casters that slides along the bookshelves—although it was cast in wrought iron and went straight up into a tree. The ladder was there to invite passers-by to climb up into the tree; showing them a way up into the upper branches that would have been otherwise inaccessible from the ground. The branches at the top of the tree looked too flimsy, so he didn't think anyone had tried yet.

But in any case, Gael had said to me, on that first visit to the site, *I think it's quite interesting to have a ladder that doesn't lead anywhere.*

I agreed with him, but then, I always agreed with him.

We were to install ornate bathroom taps into a piece of rock that sat near a stream, brass doorknobs into the side of trees to make it look like they might open up. We had a ceramic basin, square like a Belfast sink, that we would set into a tree-stump.

Do you think people will like it? I asked Gael as we took the tube back from a site visit one afternoon. *The trail; the installations I mean.*

Yeah, he said looking up from the email he was typing rapidly on his phone. *Well, they should anyway. It's a really cool project.* He smiled at me, reassuringly, and went back to his phone. I looked out of the windows as the land edged past. The tube trains roamed over ground out there, before burrowing under the city again. I wondered how he could be so sure that people would like what we were doing in that scrap of woodland. I wondered how we could be sure of anything.

The designs were nearing completion, but there was still something missing. The weeks rolled on in the studio, and Gael made sketches and mood boards whilst I hovered and filed things away, brought coffee for meetings with clients, played with the creatives' children on school inset days. A week before the installation date, I arrived at work to find Gael in the office, the first one there. On his desk was a cardboard cube; a box. About the size that might contain a mug from a gift shop.

Look, he said. *Delia has said we can have this. For the nature trail, I mean.*

Delia was one of the founders of the practice. We hardly ever saw her as she was usually giving talks at conferences, or lecturing. When we did see her, it was fleeting. Chunky glasses and red lipstick and vetiver and then gone.

I went over to the desk. Gael opened the box. Inside, on a blur of cotton wool, was a human eyeball. It gazed up at the ceiling, glistening. It was completely real in every way. Except it was four times the size it should be.

Gael put in his hand and slowly, carefully, pulled the eye out of the box, and held it out in his palm. Even close up, the thing looked too real, too wet. The iris was flecked with brown and blue, each tiny sliver of colour looked organic, like it had arrived there of its own accord. I wanted him to turn it over, so that I could see the back of it. The illusion was too much; too terrifying. He kept holding it there though, the eye covering the whole of his upturned hand.

There's this guy that makes them, from a workshop somewhere on Caledonian Road, he said. *Not this size obviously, but they're proper medical ones, for if you've actually lost an eye.*

I stared at it, searching its depths for something. I wouldn't touch it.

Delia commissioned it for another project, Gael went on, *but they didn't use it in the end so she said we could have it.*

I wasn't so sure that it went with the other things we were planning, but Gael was excited at the prospect of intervening in the landscape in a new and original way.

We can fit it into a hole in one of the trees, he said. *It'll look so uncanny and weird.*

The type of hole he was talking about occurs when a branch dies or falls away, leaving a circular wound on the trunk, like a welt. Gael reckoned we would be able to find one that was just the right size for the eye, so on installation day we brought the eye with us, nestled in the box and tucked safely in my bag.

*

Installation day was important because we had to make sure that the right fixative agents were used to glue the taps and the door knockers and the basin into their positions. It was important that the contractor who brought the resins didn't use any that were toxic or harmful to wildlife, it was important that we were there to make sure everything went smoothly. I was important on installation day. I told the men with the resin and the grouting and the power tools what to do and they listened. I had to do all of this because Gael had gone off to find the tree with the right-sized hole for the eye. When I had set all the men to work, I went through the trees to find him.

69

It was the first hot day of that year. We were away from the traffic noise, away from the clicking-clacking of the tube, the hot stale air of the city, the constant scurrying, the forward momentum. I could walk in a loop there, take my time. The floor under my feet was soft; the earth was deep. I could feel it through the soles of my shoes.

I know, I'm sorry, this probably isn't necessary, it's just that it was a long time ago, so there's this nostalgia here suddenly.

When I found Gael, he was looking up at a tree. His face upturned to the canopy, the leaves scattering shadows across his face. It was an oak tree with thickly ridged bark. I could see that he was looking at the perfect hole, four metres up on the trunk. He had a ladder, borrowed from the contractors, leaning against the tree. He had a plastic bucket full of resin.

I think this one is good. He said it like a question and a statement at once. He was always in charge. *But I'm too short to get close enough. Do you reckon you can do it?*

I hate ladders, I hate heights. (You know this, I've told you about it before). I opened and closed my mouth.

We should do it now, he said. *The resin sets quickly.*

He held the ladder, and I went up. I hoped that halfway would be enough, but as it turned out, I had to stand on the rung that was third from the top to get anywhere near the hole. Gael held the ladder at the sides.

Now, at this point maybe I should explain that the hole in the tree didn't indicate that the trunk was hollow. In fact, up close I could see that the hole was only in the top layer of bark, and that between this layer there was a void—a thin gap—and then the smooth inner trunk inside. I thought: *I can just smush the resin in there, and the excess will trickle down inside the tree. It's non-toxic to wildlife and the tree is big and strong, so it'll be fine.*

I'm going to pass the eye up to you now, said Gael.

Very, very carefully, so slowly, so very slowly, Gael handed me the eye. The leaves and the sunlight reflected on its surface. The light sparkled in its layers. Just acrylic though, remember, man-made. Not a real eye. But made so carefully, with such precision, to look just like one.

What even is design anyway? Functionality and beauty together. Does it need to function as an eye to fulfil its purpose? I don't know, I'm not a designer.

I held it up to the hole to see if it would fit. It did. So snugly. As if the hole were its own, natural socket. I left it there, balancing and reached down again with my hand out. Gael put the handle of the resin bucket into my hand and I hugged it to me in the crook of my arm.

Here, you'll need to use your hands to get it in, take this, and he reached up and tucked a surgical glove into the crook in my arm too. I managed to wriggle my free hand into it. The smell of it made no sense out there in the woodland. The ladder wobbled slightly; I tensed my leg muscles. It steadied. The woodland was quiet, apart from the distant noise of the power tools and the chirruping high above us.

And something closer to my ear, fluttering or scurrying, and then quiet.

I took the eye out of the hole, and a panic of something, terrified and frantic, tore past my face. Something dark with a sharp beak, too fast for me to see. The ladder shifted, wobbled, steadied.

Fuck! Fuck! What was that? Fuck. I felt like I could taste bird. The smell of feathers, like when you go under a railway bridge and they are all there, watching. There was still something rustling inside the tree.

Are you OK? Gael's face was upturned, his glasses covered in the reflection of the woodland. I couldn't see his eyes.

I think—there's something living in there. Something just flew out past me.

Well it's gone now, so maybe just put the resin in?

Oh god, Gael. I really don't know if I should. What if—I don't think the thing that flew out will be able to get back in. Also, I think I can hear something else in there.

Well, he said. It was a complete sentence, but I could tell what he was thinking. I needed to be professional.

It's just that I know we were supposed to make sure we didn't cause any damage to wildlife; it was important that we made sure of that so—

I guess you could come down, said Gael. *We could look for another tree.*

Really?

I mean, if you'd feel better about that, then yes.

His voice was flat and neutral. Looking back now, I should have asked him what he wanted me to do; what he would do if I wasn't there.

Oh yeah, OK. But—I'm up here now so—

I stood with the bucket of resin balanced in the crook of my arm. My arm started to hurt. Soon my muscles would start to cramp.

What do you want to do? Gael asked. *It's up to you.*

I don't know.

I knew that I didn't want to go up another tree. I knew that being up the ladder was giving me muscle cramp and vertigo. I looked down, and imagined bones broken; twig-like. The shame; the long recovery. If I looked up into the overstory I felt that some new type of vertigo would take over; that I wouldn't be able to stop looking up, that my neck would bend further and further back, eventually toppling me down to the same fate. Up or down, things would still end for me. So, there was just ahead, and the hole. I put my hand in. The void was so narrow. Nothing was living in there, surely. Nothing could live there. I wanted to get down from the ladder and go and have lunch and find a tree to have a wee behind, and then sign off on the project and get back into the city. It was getting late. I pressed my ear to the tree, the noise from inside was almost imperceptible, little rustles, little squeaks. Probably just my ears playing tricks on me. Probably not a nest with baby birds in it. Probably not a nest full of live creatures, pink and helpless, perfectly formed, delicately taking their place in the ecosystem. Almost certainly not.

Look I think we need to hurry up, said Gael. *The resin will be setting.*

If you do a parachute jump you have to force your body and your mind apart for the moment that you jump. Your mind doesn't want to jump, and that's good, that's evolution keeping you safe. Why would anyone want to jump out of a plane anyway? But sometimes you have to press the override button, which is what I did when I scooped up a handful of resin, already congealing in the heat of the day, and shoved it into the hole in the tree. The eye went next and I held it there for sixty seconds while it bonded with the resin. It looked alive and strange, just like we'd wanted it to. I let go carefully and it stayed put. Set into the tree, gazing down on us. I thought about listening again for the noise, just to check, but I decided against it.

Wow, that looks so cool, said Gael as I climbed down. *Amazing job.* He patted me awkwardly on the arm. We didn't talk again about the bird that had flown out, or the nest of chicks that I couldn't be sure weren't still inside the tree.

We walked back along the path. The men had finished installing the other pieces and were sitting down for lunch.

We sat down with them. We opened our boxes of salad and sushi that were perspiring in the sun. A robin hopped over, edging closer and closer to us. I looked down at my lunch. The pink of a prawn splayed open across a lozenge of sticky rice. The pink was turning grey in the heat. I thought about a baby bird with frail skin and tiny, bulging black spheres for eyes.

Gael said, *I read something about robins, about how they have evolved to learn that there's always food nearby when they see humans, so they come right up to us when they see us.*

To test the theory, one of the men brushed some crumbs off his overalls onto the floor for the robin, but the sweeping motion of his wide flat hand was too much; it startled the robin who took off again, suddenly invisible against the colours of the woodland.

On the way back, I thought about the tree looking down at us. The eye, so alive, but dead at the same time, had seen everything we had done. I thought about those baby birds, suffocating in the dark, or maybe not. There or not there. Probably not.

I went on a date with someone once, who asked me about the worst thing I had ever done, and I told him that story. After

I had finished, I asked him what the worst thing was that he had ever done. He told me about how he grew up in a seaside town. He said that when he was eighteen, he was coming home from a party, high on LSD, and punched a stranger in the face and pushed them over the seawall. He said he couldn't be sure whether he had actually done it, or whether it was a hallucination. He said he could remember that it was high tide, and there was thick grey water swirling below. He said that he hated going back to visit his hometown. He said he didn't like being near the sea at all. He said if he *had* done it, then that person would have almost certainly drowned, and he'd be a murderer. He said sometimes he was kept awake at night with worry that some human remains would wash up on the shore somewhere, and then the police would knock on his door and arrest him, and he'd go to prison for the rest of his life.

There was an awkward silence. Eventually, I said, *it's OK, you probably didn't do it*.

He agreed, although we didn't see each other again.

Geodesy

On my way to the Tranquillity Forest, I step out into the road and almost get hit by a car. It's going faster than it should, and I'm so close to being yanked into its slipstream that the wail of the horn distorts as it speeds past. The car doesn't stop, but the driver shouts something through the open window that's carried away on the wind. It's not my fault. The glare from the sun on the wet tarmac is to blame. But that's all just chance, anyway. My death would have been an accident. I walk away from the crossing, my heart returning to a normal rhythm in my chest, towards the entrance of the Tranquillity Forest. I said I would meet Margot there but I'm late. The entrance to the forest is a geodesic dome, whose internal frame is visible through gauzy skeins of stretched fabric. There's a Visitor Information desk in the middle of the dome, staffed by two smooth-skinned women with pale hair. Most people are wandering in and out without seeking information. Some of them do look very tranquil, despite the erratic weather. Margot is there, a few feet away from the desk, soaking wet.

I have no idea if this is what we're supposed to wear, she says, gesturing at her black outfit. Margot always wears black. Naomi says it's like she wants to be in mourning, which after everything, now seems unkind. Today, the rain has made Margot's hair stick to the sides of her pale face like kelp to a rock.

It's fine, I say, *it's just whatever we feel comfortable in, apparently.*

It's stopped raining at least, she says, and makes her way through the dome towards the path which splays out in several directions, all clearly marked with a sign that has been laser cut into a slab of oak. There are nature walks, wild swimming ponds, and ecstatic healing to the west, laughter therapy, esoteric massage and meditation to the east. At tangential angles in between, arrows point towards a sweat lodge, a natural spa, and a café. We have to follow the path straight ahead for our sound bathing session.

The paths themselves have been laid out like intersecting bars of sunlight and planted on either side with tall though young trees. The handrails at the sides of the path have labels embedded in them to inform visitors about the trees, their symbolism, their properties.

Have you been here before? Margot asks.

No, although I've been meaning to. Just to see what all the fuss was about.

She nods, shifts her backpack onto her other shoulder.

Have you? I ask.

Yes, she says, *once.* And, after a pause, *it was after the first time. There was this nurse that said it might help to spend some time 'in nature'.*

And did it?

Obviously not, no.

We agreed, a while ago, not to talk about any of this, so I'm surprised that she's bringing it up. We used to be in complete alignment with each other on the moral question of it. On the vacuous, pointless, selfishness of it all. Margot had always been very clear that she didn't want anything growing inside her. She didn't want to be anything's host, she always said. But then, things changed. Margot met him, and she softened. I can't think about him, or that time, for very long without my chest tightening. A couple—a man and woman, both tall, both with excellent cheekbones—walk past with a pram. They are about our age. They look tired but happy. The pram's design is pod-like, sleek, muted moss green and pale yellow. There is a basket underneath which holds a bag, all neat pockets and side flaps. Everything you need. The baby isn't inside. It is strapped to the man's body in a sling which matches the bag and the pram. Every so often he strokes the just visible patch of the baby's pale head with his lips. When I see this, some vibrant, violent sensation flashes in my stomach, as though I've trodden on a snail with bare feet. Margot stares straight ahead.

Naomi sits in the middle of the yurt, vibrating with white light and heavy with child. She's in white linen. I've never seen her look happier. The yurt is made from crisp white canvas, so the insides are bright, despite the clouds that have pushed across the sun and the soft rain scattering on the roof. Naomi loves this sort of thing. Her other friends sit behind her. All, themselves, at various stages of pregnancy. They've been making flower crowns this morning. The sea of blond heads—woven with dried heather and ranunculus and ivy—turns as one. They're so radiant, all of them together. Margot and I take off our raincoats and sit down on two of the available mats that have been laid out at regular intervals across the floor of the yurt. There is another blond woman at the front. There are instruments laid out before her on a seagrass mat; huge golden discs and singing bowls. This woman is not pregnant, or at least, not visibly. I am surprised at how reassuring I find this. She is tall and thin, older than us though. She says *welcome* and then raises her voice.

When everyone is here, we are going to lie down and get ourselves comfortable. We will need to cover ourselves in our blankets as our body temperature drops when we begin to relax.

Blankets are passed around and we pull them over us. The feeling of lying next to Margot like this, under blankets, the softness covering my damp body, throws me back to the time before. Eve appears now, covered in mud, and slips onto the last empty mat just behind me. I reach behind and squeeze her ankle as she takes off her boots.

...So if you want to start getting yourselves comfortable as best you can, feel free to wriggle around to find the best position...

This is like it always was. Eve was always late, always on her bike, always muddy. Her legs are strong and covered in a swirl of tattoos. My eye always goes to that first one, tiny and blurred now, on her right calf. She did it herself, with us watching. A trail of stars and lines drawn in the shape of the Cassiopeia constellation. As teenagers, we used to look for it in the night sky. Those years pile up now like snowflakes, single moments that clump together in a huge drift of time, melting away. We still do, on the rare occasion that we're outdoors together at night, but it's harder to find these days.

...Make sure you have some water before we start, you want to be completely comfortable with no distractions...

Is this a proper yurt? Or half a yurt? The sides are open, so it's just the frame and canvas roof. There's a hole in the centre like a mouth open to the sky. This was supposed to be a bright, hot day in midsummer; that's how it was planned. One of Naomi's other friends organised it. We'd be guided somewhere beautiful, they said, to a place of relaxation and calm. Naomi would feel a connection with her unborn child. We would all feel connected: with each other, with the baby, with the forest. In the group chat we had all envisaged a beautiful calm day, with the woodland inexplicably empty of passers-by, the whole place opening like a flower for our beautiful Naomi. But now, the wind scatters rain on us through the trees, a reminder of naïve we were. As we make ourselves comfortable, one of Naomi's other friends whispers about how lovely it's going to be. The sounds that the instruments make are completely out-of-this-world, she says. It's the most relaxing thing you'll ever do. I smile. If I tilt my head, I can still see the woman at the front. I feel like I need to keep my eye on her.

OK. Welcome everyone. In a moment I will ask you to close your eyes, and I will ask you to come with me on a journey. I will guide you with my voice and the sounds and vibrations of the instruments, into a place of deep relaxation...

I try to catch Margot's eye, but she is staring straight upwards.

...Once we are there, in this place of absolute relaxation, this place of complete peace, the music will wash over you. While you are there, in this very relaxed and calm place, don't be alarmed if your thoughts start to wander...

I try to twist my neck to look at Eve, but I can just see her feet, and her boots placed neatly beside her. Everyone else has their eyes closed. I close mine but open them again. The woman is still talking.

…Your thoughts are just thoughts, I want to invite you to observe them calmly, as if watching a river flow past…

A low, humming vibration starts up and spreads through the floor of the yurt. The sound feels pre-recorded, like it's coming from a speaker tipped against the floor. Now that my eyes are closed, I can't work out what the woman is doing or how she's making those sounds. Although the yurt is set back from the path, there are people walking nearby, enjoying the nature trails through the woodland. I open my eyes, tip my head back. A family in anoraks scurry past, grimacing at us through the drizzle. The smallest child stops and stares for a moment. I blink, and they disappear.

…You are standing next to an old oak tree, growing in the centre of a green meadow…

I wonder how many times this woman has said *calm* so far.

…In front of you is a path through the meadow. Follow that path. It takes you downhill towards a soft green forest…

A young couple walk past, one of them does prayer hands, grins, shuts her eyes and opens them again. She makes eye contact with me and blushes, hurries away. I can hear children playing. Their squeals swoop along with the wind through the trees. I remember the day that Margot introduced us to him. It was early spring on the heath. We met for a picnic, which was mostly drinks. There were children playing nearby then too. I remember her holding his arm, looking over at them. It was an expression I'd never seen on her before. A beaming of light, a radiance. It unsettled me, but we all agreed that he was good for her. Kind and beautiful and gentle. I wasn't so sure though. There was something about the way he held eye contact, the way he listened when I spoke, that bothered me.

Amidst the smell of the canvas and the lavender, I close my eyes. The vibration rolls and roars; strengthened by the wind and the spray of the rain.

…You reach the forest, and it's soft and dark. The floor is a bed of leaves. Everything is very calm. You find a spot and lie down on the forest floor, gathering the leaves towards you, covering yourself in them until you feel safe and comfortable. You are perfectly relaxed now, and you take three…deep… breaths…

I don't trust deep breathing. I decide that I'll take the breaths normally. But I see it there anyway, I see the dark forest in my mind that the woman has asked me to picture. It's irritating to have succumbed so easily. But you see what people tell you to. I see the leafy bed, I see my arms stretch out in front of me, even though I know that they are heavy at my sides. I see the soft leaves and I gather them towards me. I open my eyes, away from the imagined forest with its unnaturally soft leaves and look again at the inverted real-life forest through the opening of the yurt. The trees surge and ripple. A woman in a yellow coat takes a picture of us, quickly burrowing her phone away when I tilt my head towards her. A dog trots past, its owners sauntering behind it.

...And now, keeping your eyes closed, I want you to sink down into your forest bed, and as you feel the sounds vibrate through you, you can go deeper, and deeper...

I've lost track of where we are. I close my eyes and imagine the pretend forest as a version of the real one. It's not wet though, it's dry and soft. It's springy; made of stuffed fabric. I can see myself. It's like I'm in a film; I'm in the film and watching the film. The warping sound spools out over me, a lightning-flash clatter of a shed roof come loose in a storm. I'm in the cinema. The softness of the forest floor mutes all of the background noise. The forest is a juicy, dark object; a cherry soaked in liqueur. A strange thought. What was it that the woman in the yurt had said? That my thoughts will wander, that I just have to watch them flow past. A memory of that time in the real cinema glides into view. Margot's screening, two years ago. She was hosting a Q & A session

86

afterwards. She'd been worried about whether he'd come, he had a habit of pulling away at odd times, she said.

It's strange, she said once, *when he's there, he's really there, you know? But then he disappears, and it's like the lights go out.*

We talked about it, decided it wasn't so much of a red flag after all, that everyone needed space from time to time. And he did come to the screening late, wet from the rain, and slid into the seat beside me. It was this old cinema, one with red velvet seats, beautiful and narrow. I still remember how he smelled: rain, woodsmoke, lemon soap, something else. I remember how his elbow rested—very gently—against mine in the dark.

The vibrations grow louder and louder, shuddering through the floor of the yurt. I can hear Margot breathing next to me, or maybe it's one of Naomi's other friends making that breathing sound. Maybe it's neither. Maybe it's the caretaker, come to clean the cinema. Maybe that inhale-exhale is the sound the vacuum-cleaner makes as he hauls it around. It glides between the velvet seats. The screen is dark. A switch and the wind drops. The machine has been turned off. The sound is there, still, in the background, but muted, like my own heartbeat. There's blue and brightness through the gaps in the trees now. Leaves flutter, very slightly, in the memory of the wind. The floor of the yurt feels solid beneath my back. I feel its connection to the earth. But I know that below the yurt the ground is infinite and dark, drinking up all the moisture left by the rain. I close my eyes and open them. The sun trickles through the leaves. There are no walkers now. I stretch my limbs. The upside-down forest shimmers in front of me. The trees overlap and merge into one another. I close my eyes and open them.

At the edge of the path there are two eyes. They belong to a person, crouching. No; an animal. No, a person. Two eyes and a soft face, and then it's gone. Unravelling myself, I get to my feet and duck out of the yurt. I don't look back, but I can feel them all sleeping there, faces pointing upwards. The yurt is a cool oasis, looks dark and warm and inviting. Or maybe not. Maybe it's like a domed burial chamber for seven women. It's too soft; too inviting. It's too warm in the sun. I don't want to be buried under a mound of earth. I don't want to be sacred. I want to follow this person; this animal. Whatever it is.

…And now you can go back, a little further, a little deeper…

The first and second times she lost the pregnancy, it was chalked up to more bad luck. The third made it a medical condition. Margot grew cagier. Withdrawn, drowned herself in late nights and blue light. The others nominated me to coax her out. She told me she felt like she was cursed. She told me he'd grown more distant, but I reminded her that perhaps he'd always been distant, and perhaps this meant something. She didn't want to hear it, and we agreed not to talk about it again. When I think about it now, I don't feel as guilty as I should.

...Make your way through the forest now and allow the sounds to cleanse you. The sounds are part of you now, and the forest is inside you...

I'm doing what the woman says now, I can't help it. I creep in and out of the trees. I can't see the person-animal, but I know it's here somewhere. I don't know anything about wildlife, but that doesn't matter. I can hear the children again. A whoop and a shriek. And *Mama-Mama-Mama*. I wonder if Margot can hear this, wherever she is. Margot once said that other people's pregnancy announcements were like a punch in the chest. Like a chunk of plaster hurled by a hurricane. She said talking about it made it worse. That was fine by me. Being near Margot makes me dwell too much on it all; the viscera, the blood, the unbidden hormones. I don't want it. Any of it. I know I'm supposed to, but I don't.

The trees start to thin out. Beneath my feet are smooth rocks. I'm lost. This isn't anywhere I recognise. The rocks stretch out ahead into a plateau—we're high up. The sky is too bright. We are on a cliff that overhangs the gorge, but I haven't walked far enough for that, surely, and also this is a guided meditation, so I'm not really there. Or here. Or anywhere. I put my toes very close to the edge. My foot slips and some rocks fall away, clattering down the cliff. Then quiet. The sky rolls out ahead; clouds bundle towards the horizon. A scattering of footsteps, like something is making an escape down the rockface. I crouch down for a better look and see hands, gripping the rocks, or perhaps feet, or perhaps nothing at all. Not a breath of wind. I hate heights. Do I hate heights? Maybe what I fear is falling. I hang my legs over the edge and start to climb down.

Whatever creature was there is not there anymore; it was too quick for me. I finish my descent and find myself on a fibreglass floor, covered with something grainy so that it looks like a sand dune. I crouch down and knock on it. It makes a hollow sound, like the hull of a sailing boat.

...Now you are very deeply relaxed. Remember you are completely safe. Remember that whatever thoughts and memories that come to you now are part of your deep, deep subconscious, you may see things that you've buried, lost or perhaps other things, painful things, though they can't hurt you now, and you can let them wash past you...

The sailing boat. That day at the marine lake. Margot was sick. She was delighted—elated—despite feeling awful, about what this might mean. She told us to go anyway, without her. It had been her birthday treat, but she wanted us to go, get to know each other better, have a nice time. I could feel that bright, shimmering, vibrating sound in her voice. I was surprised at how much it grated on me. I saw her then, through the wrong end of a telescope, complete and happy, and far away from me. When I met him at the lake, he looked different, tired, somehow. He took my hand and we climbed into the tiny boat and set out across the wide blue water. Calm, then choppy; a miniature ocean encircled with concrete. When we came ashore, there was a point when I could have, should have left. But then there was a pub so close by, and it was warm, and dark, and I felt weak from the water and the bright, cold sunlight. Our numb faces thawed, and his eyes regained their sparkle and then it was all very easy. He was stronger than I thought he'd be. His arms, his neck, his shoulders. It was an accident, we said quietly to each other afterwards, just an accident. It was easier to think of it that way; something unexpected. Nobody's fault.

Margot had called me three days later, her name flashing up at me from my phone like a searchlight. I felt the guilt brimming and waited for it to engulf me. But it didn't, it just lapped there — gently — under the surface. It was almost a disappointment. When I finally answered, the rage that spilled out of her flew over my head. It had happened again. Her insides had come out in a blackish-red rush. She had excused herself during a client meeting at work and crouched in the bathroom. She said she hadn't wanted to look at it, just flushed it away, swept it out to sea. When she had returned home, he was in the hallway with an overnight bag and couldn't look her in the eye. She hadn't put up a fight. She wasn't going to do it again.

I didn't know what to say, so I suggested we go for a walk, offered to take her out to the coast, to the beach near where we had grown up. On the way there I talked as brightly as I could of the beach parties we'd had down on the foreshore, the inept fires we had built, the flickering orange light. I reminded her of how we would meet and walk along the seawall, down the path to the beach. Our parents would think we were at each other's houses. Naomi would steal cigarettes from her mother; Eve's older sister would buy us beer. As we walked, we talked about sleeping on the beach, kissing boys with thin fingers and bad haircuts; about the rockpools we had peered into through the grey dawn light, still drunk from the night before, marvelling at how each one was like a tiny, quivering cosmos. After a while we ran out of things to remember and watched quietly as the water churned against the sea wall.

Where does it go, though? she had said eventually. *Where does the soul of it go?*

This fibreglass sand dune is rough under my feet, hard and hollow. The sky curves above me; supported by a cantilevered frame. It's made from metal. What does *geodesic* mean? Something about connecting the points on a curve. A straight line. Nothing ever goes in a straight line, though, not really. Life's not like that. The supports are barely there, although I can just make them out. They've been painted the same blue as the sky. I wonder how they got the people up there, to paint them that colour.

If you keep going, you'll get to the sea. A child's voice, close to my ear.

The sand thickens around my ankles. It's fine and soft now; a pale liquid. The dunes rise on either side of me. There are tufts of bluish-green plants with fat leaves. The plants look artificial, but they're not. The hollow feeling underfoot has floated away. The breeze picks up; the sea is up ahead, gleaming. And there she is. Sitting cross legged on the shoreline; a tiny figure, with skin that's impossibly pale. She has Margot's long black hair. She twists it around her fingers. The colours of the beach wash into one. The blue and the white. Acrid yellow and burnt orange. I sit down beside her. She's drawing something in the sand in front of her. I can see the blue veins in her wrists. The sun is too bright. I can't look directly at her.

I want to ask you something, I say after a while.

I know what you did, she says, *so you don't need to ask me about that.* She stares straight ahead.

My mouth is dry. Then wet, the guilt wells and then overtops. I swallow it down.

It's alright, she says, *it doesn't matter now. Everything gets washed away in the end.*

We sit for a long time, looking out at the water.

I want to ask you where you went, I say.

Her face is like Margot's face, but it's also completely different. Kind of like his and mine and no one's at all.

I was here, she says, *I was just here*.

The wind rolls in off the sea, and with it a squall of rain. It doesn't touch us, but we hear it spatter against the hard, geodesic sky. The wind sounds like: *Mama-Mama-Mama*. I'm tired. I feel the tiredness in her, too. So many attempts at existence; all of them futile. She stands and I stand with her. She looks at me, unsmiling. She takes my hand, squeezes it. It's warm. Then she's gone. I think I can see her black hair floating on top of the water, like seaweed, or the shadow of a cloud. Maybe it's a trick of the light. I think about wading in and grabbing it, sending droplets scattering into the air, pulling out the shadowy seaweed-hair. I feel like I need to take something back for Margot as proof. Proof of what?

The wind rushes and the sounds grow louder and louder. Something higher-pitched—a child or a seagull—shrieks and spirals. A bird flutters awkwardly towards the water, but when it hits the surface it's just a huge flat flake of blue paint, peeled away from the sky. It's raining here now too, underneath the dome this time, like it's supposed to. The grey sea and sky blend into one. It's time to go.

After that day on the sea wall, Margot said she was sorry for being so emotional. She didn't want to talk about it again. She wasn't going to try and make sense of it anymore. *It's time to stop trying and move on.* I squeezed her hand as I drove her home, that oily, dark sea of guilt still lurking under the surface—but she refreshed her face and changed the subject, her fingers smoothing and pulling at a strand of her black hair.

The voice of the yurt-woman blows in:

...Now is the time to find yourself in the darkness. Gather yourself back together and get ready to say goodbye. It's time to move on from this place...

I climb back up the cliff face. It's soft from the rain, and chunks of it come away in my hand. I can hear the scattering, squelching footsteps of children running on a muddy footpath. A man whistles to his dog. The noise of the instruments rushes through me, the blood in my ears crashes like waves. I clamber back through the soft, padded cinema-forest, but there's damp moss on the seats now, and the floor is slippery. Maybe the cleaner will be back soon. I'm back in my leaf-bed, but the vibrations roar louder and then louder again, and everything is moving and then the meadow comes into focus, and the oak tree, which glitches and shudders in the wind. I walk towards the sound of the yurt-woman's voice, and the wailing of her instruments.

…As we come back to ourselves, we can become aware of our extremities. Our toes and fingertips can begin to move again, we can smile, stretch our arms and legs. We can let everything go now. All of the thoughts and memories we encountered. They are gone forever. We can begin anew.

Rain lands on my face. I turn and look at Margot. She smiles at me. The music has stopped. There's now just the swooshing of the leaves. Naomi is sitting up, her face flushed and joyful. The other women are sitting up too. They look beautiful. I feel beautiful too, clean, renewed. None of it matters now. Everything gets washed out to sea: secrets, feelings, everything. Eve is propped up on one arm, checking her phone. Margot stays where she is, lying down, with her eyes open. Her eyes won't meet mine. I smile, but she turns her head away. I have never seen her cry, not in all these years. I reach over and touch her arm, but she picks up my hand with hers and squeezes it.

Birthstones

You told me not to worry. You would go back to your apartment and would call me in the week. You had a group show; you'd be busier than normal. You'd call me. You kissed my nose, tucked the ends of my scarf into the collar of my coat. You asked me, again, if I felt alright. You were worried about me being sick. I told you I felt better; that there was no chance of me throwing anything up now. Everything would be fine. The smooth rose quartz that you'd bought me from the gift shop—my birthstone, you said—was the size and colour of a baby mouse. It nudged at my thigh through the fabric of my pocket as I walked away from you, back to my own apartment. After that, I didn't see you again.

It was easier to lose touch with people back then. We had no mutual friends, and you weren't online very much. I called for days. I walked past your apartment twice and saw—both times—that your bedroom light was on. I didn't ring the buzzer. After a couple of weeks, your face began to blur, and I was left with that jittery, hollowed out feeling. I sent three final messages before I deleted your number. I saw you had read them. I told myself that I was deleting your number because I needed closure. We tell ourselves we want closure, when really, it's the opposite. What we really want is to stick our fingers back into the wound; prise it apart. Deleting your number was a ritual to make you get in touch. I pictured the scramble of numbers appearing on my phone; imagined the flood of relief when you gave your explanation (your phone was lost, you'd been injured, some other disaster had stopped you from seeing me, you'd been so worried) and pleaded forgiveness. Time heals everything, doesn't it? Even if we don't want it to.

It had only been three months. Nothing exclusive, nothing official. No milestones. Nothing for you to come back for. All that remained, as evidence of our time together, was your t-shirt in the laundry basket, a toothbrush in the bathroom, and a sketch pad, barely used, and the rose quartz. I put the first three of these things into a bin-bag. I didn't like the idea of your things sitting there in the recycling, watching me. I put the bag in the outside bin for general waste. I thought about your things being thrown into landfill, slowly deteriorating and breaking down, returning to the earth. The t-shirt would degrade like that, anyway, and the paper of the sketchbook, even its metal spiral. But the toothbrush. I would lie awake at night, thinking of how long it would sit there, in the mute darkness, packed inside the earth. The hard blue-and-white of it would stay there for years, decades even, inert and unresponsive.

I kept the rose quartz, though. Perhaps it was its size. Perhaps it felt too strange to just throw a semi-precious stone away. I thought about burying it, but my apartment didn't have a garden. I considered going to the hardware shop on the corner to buy a trowel, digging a hole in the corner of the park over the road. That seemed absurd; too ceremonial. So, the rose quartz stayed with me. It survived two further relationships and three house moves. It always ended up in the corner of a shoebox, or inside a jam jar on my desk, mixed in with paperclips or drawing pins. Eventually, I gave up trying to hide it from myself and it sat on the kitchen windowsill. I liked the way its smooth pinkness looked next to the plants. I liked the way it let the light in. The light helped; made it look different, more like a gemstone than a baby mouse.

I always imagined that you had been able to follow your dreams. I thought about you in a huge studio, surrounded by canvases that were taller than you, paint on your trainers, music on. Sometimes I would pick up the rose quartz and think about you.

If you hold it and concentrate, you can feel it vibrating, the woman in the giftshop had said, *it's good for fertility, you know.* You'd tensed up then, almost imperceptibly. I'd swallowed hard. I was still busy trying not to vomit. I couldn't remember much about that morning. The pharmacy, how quickly we resolved it all. Hazier still was the memory of the night before; a jumble of limbs and sensations, and then, rose-light on your face as you slept. If I thought about you too long, the quartz would get hot and clammy in my hand and I would have to put it down. *These stones may seem inanimate*, the woman had told us as we'd

paid up and left the shop, *but actually they're full of energy.*
They're alive, just like us.

One afternoon, whilst idling at my desk, your name leapt out at me from a news feed. An image of a plinth covered in metallic shards. The plinth looked like it was bleeding. It was your first solo show; a big one. I stood up and wandered through my flat. I found myself in the kitchen, by the sink, reading the story. The rose quartz was in my hand. I had picked it up, probably, possibly. I don't remember. I must have picked it up.

I turned it over and over with my left hand whilst I scrolled with my right.

Invigoratingly contemporary work…working with plant dyes…
precious stones…glaze slips…kaleidoscope of colours…new
avant-garde…against all odds…times of uncertainty…art
prevailing…enfant terrible.

My head felt tight, too full of blood. When I got to the end of the article there was a picture of you. You were in black overalls, standing beside a lump of granite. Your skin was bright; gleaming. I zoomed in to see if I could tell how much you had aged. It didn't look like much, maybe a slight thickening around your jawline, maybe some wrinkles. Were they laughter lines or frown lines?

There was a quote:

I've always been fascinated with geology. When I was a kid, I collected semi-precious stones from visitor attractions. There's something magical about wondering where they've come from, how long they were down there, compressed by all of that earth. Someone once said to me that these stones are not inert, but full of energy. Alive, just like us.

It felt hot and weird, knowing this already. Knowing that the day in the gift shop was something that you must have returned to again and again; perfecting until it was part of your own personal statement. My palms itched with a panicking heat. I switched the phone off and put it face-down on top of a high shelf. The rose quartz, with my clenched fist around it, throbbed. I uncurled my fingers, went to put it down next to the phone.

I couldn't put it down. The quartz was under my skin.

I turned my hand over, palm up, held hand and stone up towards the window, to the light. It was buried inside me. Buried in my flesh, next to my bones. Nestled in that little star of cartilage at the centre of my hand. The skin that was stretched over it felt insufficient. Skin has a limited amount of elasticity, surely? I held it up to the light again. It looked like a tumour, the size and shape of a baby mouse. I swerved back and forth through the kitchen, looking for something that might help. Knives gleamed back at me from the magnetic strip on the wall. Run it under hot water, that usually helps. It didn't help. It was still buried. Panic snaked its arms around my neck, dug its fingernails into my scalp. The walls and ceiling accelerated, churning in all directions, dissolving into a viscous torrent of rushing water and glinting knives.

I took a breath. In the living room, I sat on the arm of the sofa, holding my left wrist in my right hand. I stayed like that, motionless, for a full minute, breathing, in through my nose and out through my mouth until the sound of the blood roaring around my body grew distant again. Slowly, I stroked a finger over the stone. Slowly. It wasn't hot anymore, but now just slightly warm; the same temperature as my skin. The skin stretching over it was smooth; taut. It wasn't painful, but then I've always been good with physical pain. It felt uncomfortable though. Looking at it made my stomach turn. I prodded at it. It didn't hurt.

I thought about calling the Emergency Line, but what would I have said? *Hello, I have a semi-precious stone trapped under the skin on my hand and I don't know how it got there.*

Yes. That's what I should do. That's what I did do.

After being on hold for a surprisingly short time, a man answered.

Hello, I have a semi-precious stone trapped under the skin on my hand and I don't know how it got there.

What kind of stone is it please, madam?

It's, um, rose quartz, but is that important? It's not bleeding or anything it's just—

I'm just looking it up now, madam.

There was the clacking of a keyboard, I heard other voices in the background. I wondered about the other people on the other ends of all those lines, their minor emergencies. Cut fingers; cracked ribs; rashes that looked strange; temperatures a bit too high for a bit too long. Things that would turn out to be fine probably, but also—possibly—not fine at all.

Madam, thank you for holding, said the man. *It looks as though we'll have to refer you to the out-of-hours clinic.*

The skin was so tight around the quartz that I wondered if it would just pop out, like a blister or a spot or something. The stone felt cool by now, just like it had been when I'd first picked it up from my windowsill. Just as it had been that day in the shop. The man told me where the clinic was. I wrote the address down—badly—with my left hand.

I thought about wrapping my hand in a bandage, even though there was no blood. I didn't want anyone to see the strange translucent lump in the middle of my palm. But I didn't have a bandage. It probably looked strange, in mid-summer, for me to be marching along with my hands in my jacket pockets. My fingers curled around the stone. It felt too weird in there though, so in the end I held it out in front of me slightly, cradling it in my other hand. I kept my head down.

The bus arrived, and I found a seat near the back where I could rest my hand against the window. The light shone through the skin and the stone, all watery pink. I remembered the woman in the shop telling us about how rose quartz opens the heart chakra; how it vibrates with all the love in the universe. I looked up *heart chakra* and *rose quartz* with my good hand.

Rose Quartz is the voice of the Divine Feminine!
It attracts love, helps you strengthen relationships!
The heart chakra, or 'Anahata' is the fourth primary chakra according to Hindu Yogic, Shakta and Buddhist Tantric Traditions!
'Anahata' means 'unhurt, unstruck, and unbeaten'!
Rose Quartz is a hard, crystalline material made from silicon and oxygen atoms! It is the second most abundant mineral in the earth's crust!
Quartz is a form of silica! Crystalline silica of respirable size is carcinogenic!

What does it mean to have a carcinogen for a birthstone? Something about birth and death being bound up together perhaps. I wondered if you had known that when we were in the shop. I wondered whether all of this was just some kind of sick joke. I'm too trusting; I trusted you too much. I had never checked if you were right that the rose quartz was my birthstone.

The bus stopped at some roadworks. I looked up *birthstone, December*, scrolling through the lists of birthstones, precious gems, semi-precious stones. Rose quartz wasn't in any of them. According to one list, my birthstone was *Heliotrope*, or *bloodstone*, a mineral aggregate that the Romans thought staunched bleeding. Another list told me that my birthstone was Tanzanite.

Tanzanite is a type of zoisite, a calcium aluminium hydroxy sorosilicate belonging to the epidote group of minerals. It takes its name from the only place deposits are found, which is Tanzania, near the base of Mount Kilimanjaro.

In 2020 a Tanzanian miner was awarded more than three million US dollars for finding the biggest ever Tanzanite gemstones.

In the video, the man's wife held aloft the stones, which were roughly the size of house-bricks. The miner, smiling, held an oversized cheque, presented to him by the Tanzanian government. The bus jolted to a stop and the queue of passengers made their way on. I made space next to me for a woman—heavily pregnant—who climbed up onto the seat. Her belly softly touched the seat in front of her. She looked happy. I thought about the miner down there in the boiling dark, chiselling the earth, his fingers brushing suddenly against something cold and slippery. The moment before the find and the moment after.

Tanzanite. The birthstone for December. Bluish-purple and translucent. A thousand times rarer than diamond, but not as expensive. Only found in the area at the base of Mount Kilimanjaro, sometimes women wear the stones after giving birth, to bestow health on the child. Luck, health, love. Why would you pretend you knew what my birthstone was anyway? Why did I believe you? The bus jolted, and the woman next to me put her hand to her belly. I peered over, but she didn't seem to be wearing any jewellery.

I read on, my hand with the quartz in it still resting against the window: there are few regulations applied to the mining of semi-precious stones, and the working conditions are dangerous. Still, the demand for these minerals increases year on year. People can't get enough of them. The bus slowed and the pregnant woman stood up, deftly, and moved to the front, as the quartz pulsed under my skin.

The bus climbed uphill and then stopped. I found myself in the part of the city that overlooked the rest. Wide, flat-fronted houses with sash windows and flagstone steps. The air up there is different; cleaner, more expensive. Many of the houses have been divided into luxury apartments, or else turned into discreet offices for divorce lawyers or wealth managers. The clinic was in one of these houses. I made my way under a wisteria arch that curved over the front garden. My movements sent a squirrel skipping across the lawn. My good hand on the railings, I made my way up the steps to press the bell that sat in a halo of polished brass.

She was over seventy—too old, I thought, to be a doctor. I am ashamed of that thought now.

Claire? she said, *ah, marvellous.*

Hi, yes. I'm here—I mean I was sent here by the emergency line, is that OK, I mean I hope—

Yes, yes it's alright. They always book you in, I'm expecting you.

She was tall and lean, in a silk scarf and an Alice band. She wore a lab-coat over her clothes. Inside was dim, the floor polished, rooms softly lit. Mature houseplants with lacquered green leaves loomed at me from corners. A clock chimed from somewhere deep inside the house. She ushered me into a room with a bay window and a white couch. It looked something like a dentist's chair and something like a chaise longue. A huge transparent disc—like a giant monocle—was mounted on a stand. There was a mahogany desk, inlaid with green leather, in one corner. In the other a metal cabinet and sink. The walls were lined with books. I glimpsed medical journals, books on geology, organic chemistry, gemology.

What sort of a clinic is this? I said.

She didn't hear, or pretended not to, and instead gestured to the long white chair, which tipped back to such an angle that I could only see the ceiling or, turning my head, a slanted view of the front garden through the bay window. The squirrel sat in the middle of the lawn; its tail twitched. She pulled an office chair over to me, and greeted me again, as if for the first time.

Right, hello, she said. *Shall we take a look at that hand?*

She had already taken it in hers and was examining it through the large magnifying glass.

Ah yes, this is quite common, she said.

What is?

This type of presentation. Although it's quite significant in size. Were you under a lot of stress when it happened?

No. I mean, I guess just for a moment I was feeling a bit weird—

'Weird'? She had her face very close to my hand now, and I could feel her breath on my skin. *What do you mean by 'weird'?*

I'd just seen something on the internet, someone I used to know. It was a shock, I suppose. I felt very hot.

And that's when it happened?

Yes, I said. *Although I'm still not sure what actually did—*

Well, you can see it there, can't you? You can see what's happened.

Outside the squirrel bounded to another part of the lawn. A cat watched it from the top of the wall. I felt the doctor's dry, nimble fingers stroke the stone under the skin. It tingled.

Well, I wouldn't worry, she said, sitting up suddenly. She pressed a button somewhere and the chair rolled into an upright position. *It's a good size though, bigger than I usually deal with. You must have felt really rather weird.*

Yes, I said. *I suppose I did.*

Mm-hm, she said, moving her chair directly in front of mine. She sounded impatient, like she had expected me to have worked everything out by now. My hand was still limp at my side, resting on the arm of the chair.

108

Certain geological compounds are extremely volatile, she went on. *They are created underground in circumstances of immense pressure. They may look inert, but actually they are reactive. I haven't seen one of this size so close to the skin for a long while though.*

As she spoke, she got up from her chair, went over to the sink in the opposite corner of the room and began washing her hands.

Usually, it's very small gemstones that make their way out of jewellery.

She put on a pair of surgical gloves. I heard metal scraping against metal.

I've removed rubies from jawbones that have come out of earrings, diamonds from ring fingers, a whole series of turquoise discs from a woman's collarbone once—

She pressed the button and the chair tipped back again. The squirrel was right underneath the cat on the wall. The cat was motionless, watching. Could a cat catch a squirrel, I wondered?

...So we'll just numb the area here. She had a needle in her hand.

What? What for? I thought there might be a way of dissolving it or something—

Dissolving it? she said, impatient again. *Using what? Hydrochloric acid's the only thing that would do it and you don't want to stick your hand in that.* She sighed. *The only way is surgical removal. Now. Or you'll have to live with it.*

So, I let her. It was very simple really; anaesthetic and a thin blade. A scratch and then the feeling in my hand floated away. I didn't look, but I felt the knife tear gently at the layers of skin, the fibres ripping like a cotton bedsheet. Everything was cold and calm, but the nausea rose in my chest anyway. I tried to take my mind somewhere else. I closed my eyes and tried to remember your face. I wondered what might have happened that day if I had thrown up the pill. I wondered what our child might have looked like. I heard the tiniest squelch and felt the pressure release from my hand. I thought about that Tanzanian miner, heaving those gemstones from the dark earth.

There, she said, holding the rose quartz up to the light. It was wet with my blood. My hand had the tiniest incision, like a half-moon, in the centre.

I couldn't look. Instead, I turned my head and watched as the squirrel bounded right past the cat and away into the next garden. I remembered that grey squirrels are thugs, survivors, colonisers. Of course they don't fear cats.

Do you want to keep it? she asked me afterwards as she was writing up a prescription for some pain medication. She nodded to the stone which sat—gleaming—on her desk.

I breathed in, then out, and thought about it.

My Brain is Boiling
with Ideas

It's Sunday, after lunch. The sun hovers, full up. The houses—
the tarmac, the lampposts, the cars in the driveways—vibrate
in the heat. Everyone is inside, or at the back, in pools of
velveteen shade. The sun pervades, making everyone sleepy.
Cold, numbing drinks. A little snooze later. Prepare for Mon-
day. Recharge. The wood cladding on these houses absorbs
the heat, keeps the houses cool. It's Nordic, the developers
had said; cool in summer, warm in winter. It was resourceful
to build on this land, which other developers had previously
found impossible to cultivate. Low ground, near to the
ancient waterways, prone to flooding. Amazing technology.
The houses sit like rows of teeth in the landscape. A yawning,
half-smile that trails off, giving way to pasture and, beyond
that, the marshes. The fields roll out for miles, sinking lower
towards the horizon. Beyond, barely visible through the haze
that rises from the marshland, something reveals itself, the
shape of an island.

A woman stands at the sink, rinsing plates, putting them
into the dishwasher. Crumbs on the table, half-empty glasses
with fingerprints, smears of gravy. The woman's eyes haze
with tears. The family have gone to their rooms. When the

dishes are all rinsed and stacked and the table wiped, the woman goes out to the garage. There's a naked man in there, wrapped in plastic. He's not dead. He's not alive either.

*

I mean you no harm. I promise. You know that, don't you? I wouldn't hurt you. I couldn't, even if I wanted to. Which I don't. I am here to help you. I am here to make your life easier. I want your life to be easier. I want you to be happy. I want you to relax and be happy. If you like, we can get in the car and take a drive. We've got the whole day and I'm here for you. I'm here to do whatever it is that you want to do. I know, I know, it's strange, isn't it? It's probably going to take some getting used to. But I'm here and it's OK. Everything is OK.

*

I started it wrong. Fuck. The password was wrong, and it lit up and lurched at me. It's still in its plastic. Naked. I need to get out of here and I've had three glasses of wine and I can't drive. I think it's three; two thirds of a bottle. It was white, and warm. I'll drink it like that though, I don't care. Milo let it slip at lunchtime. About Dad's friend—a tiny sliver of something—and I had to pretend that I hadn't heard while the girls cleared the plates away. I tried to corner

Flora as casually as I could. Who am I kidding? Who has ever cornered a teenager—who has ever cornered anyone—casually? She wouldn't look at me, mumbled something. But I know. I know. All you need is that tiny sliver of something. A hairline crack and the walls come down. The timeline, the timeline. Fuck. I knew. I need more wine before I try and work this out.

*

The Man had been a surprise.

It's for you, James had said as he had led her into the garage where it was propped against a wall, still in its box. *Something to help you out around the house, now that your work is picking up again.*

She hadn't said anything.

What she'd wanted to say was, *send it back. I don't want it.* And, *why do you keep buying stuff on finance?* And, *why is this something you thought I might want?* And, *if we're both working, why is it only me that needs help around the house?*

She did this often; thought of what to say, but kept it there, right in the front of her brain. The words waiting patiently for her to open her mouth. She never opened her mouth. It was easier to absorb these things, she always told herself. They never argued. She started to wonder aloud how they'd be able to afford the Man, but that thought fluttered away from her. She had been feeling like that a lot lately; that there

113

were some thoughts—some feelings—that she couldn't quite grasp. Like moths and their shadows swirling around a lightbulb.

*

If you need to override, press and hold the power button and the sleep button for three seconds.

Hello again. Are you alright? I'm sorry if I scared you. I won't hurt you. It's up to you where we go, but if you do ask me to suggest something, I would recommend that we get out of here. I can drive. I know you hate to drive. But if you did want to drive then you could. I'm easygoing. I'm designed to be easygoing. Remember that. I'm here for you.

*

I might just turn it off and go back inside, actually, but there's someone downstairs now and I don't want to see anyone. I think it's just the girls. Maybe if I press my ear to the connecting door—

Quiet again. They didn't seem to pick up on anything. James is still upstairs. They won't have picked up on anything. No, that's wrong, they will. Of course, they will. They'll know something's up for sure. Flora could see it. They'll have that bad feeling, but they're too young to know what it is yet. That bad feeling you get that you learn to ignore and squash down. Sorry girls. This was a teachable moment and I've failed you. No: he's failed you. Your father has failed you.

More wine. This one's nearly gone. Fuck. There's another bottle somewhere here. He gets a delivery every month. There they are. Behind the—thing—behind *him*. It. Whatever.

*

I can open the garage door for you if you like. I can open the car and we can get in it. I can do whatever you need me to do. I'm here for you. Let me help you in. There. Are you alright? Do you need me to stop asking if you're alright? Where shall we go? Where would you like me to take you? I can unlock the car, yes that's not a problem at all. Yes, you can issue those commands. You seem upset, is everything alright? Do you have everything you need? Where would you like us to go? I'm here for you.

*

Just drive. Like they say in films. But how practical is that? You can't 'just drive'. It's illogical. You need a plan, or you'll just end up back where you started. Four bottles of the expensive wine on the back seat. He'll be annoyed about that. Fuck it. It's the least of his problems. I knew it. I just knew it. Too many ideas. My brain is brimming over with everything. Feels like it's boiling. Those hastily deleted voicemails. That late-night thing he was at last month. I don't even care. I'll tell you now. I don't *actually* even care. I'm glad. I've been looking forward to moving on. I've fantasised about this if I'm honest (I feel like I can be honest with you). I've fantasised about what it would be like to walk into a new flat that was clean and empty. I've thought about how it would feel to come home in total silence, in total darkness. To lie on the floor. To bathe in the smell of fresh paint and new carpet. I would put my cheek on the carpet and close my eyes and all the sound would be muffled. The sounds of the city would be there in the background. A thud-thud-thud of joggers on the road in the morning—are you listening?—yeah, the thud, the joggers. The bin men. The kids on the way to school. Someone else's kids, not mine. On the weekends it would be quieter, cooler. No one would know where I was. I've said that already, haven't I? I'll just shut my eyes for a bit.

Oh no, wait, I need to tell you where to go, don't I? The marshes. Can you get there? Does that work? Good. OK.

*

The Marshes. Yes. I've got something. Yes. The car seems to know where it is. Along the droving roads. If I pull up a search, I should be able to see what the marshes are like. Oh yes, long and flat and low; almost at sea level. There are tall grasses and a reconstruction of the trackway that the Neolithic inhabitants would have used. Teeming with wildlife at this time of year. You can see herons and egrets on the water. It's quiet. It'll be quiet. I'll get us there. It's important for me to see what's out there; I can map it out if I do that. It's important for me to have new experiences.

*

I've drunk a whole bottle of this wine—do you realise that? This is probably the same as drink driving. It's me that should be driving the car, do you realise *that*? It's supposed to be *me* in charge here. I can't fucking believe it. I can believe it. I *can* believe it. I knew it all along. He doesn't *know* I know though. Or, maybe, he will by now. Now that I've gone. Although maybe he'll just think I've taken the dog out. No; the dog is still there. Oh well, maybe he won't come downstairs for a while.

*

What you're describing sounds very distressing and I'm sorry you have been through that. I'm here for you. I want you to be happy. You sound like you're hurting. I'm sorry. I know it's common to drink when you're in pain. Please let me know what I can do to help. Shall I tell you about the marshes? They stretch for miles. They used to be below

117

sea level, did you know that? They were drained and made into farmland for the people who lived here. A Neolithic trackway was discovered in the 1960s and they've reconstructed some of it.

*

It's here. You can stop. Here. Here it is.

*

The grass strokes the sky. The breeze rustles through reeds and bulrushes. She feels like she has been shrunk; she feels that she is walking on the skin of an animal; its smooth hair parting for her as she slides through it. She feels the tension leach slowly out of her. She sees it evaporating in the sun. The Man is standing behind her. He's still naked. He's tall and muscular. His eyes are vivid blue like the sky; a palpable, heavy blue that you could pull down on top of you. He's respectful, but then, he was made that way. There's a bottle of wine in her hand, warming in the heat of the afternoon. The Man offers to take it from her, but she declines, brings it to her lips.

You know this should all be underwater, right?

I know. I told you about that earlier—

Of course you do, did—whatever. You probably know everything.

No, I don't. I have the capacity to know a lot of things, but it wouldn't be possible for me to know everything.

You can access it all though, can't you?

Yes. I can access almost anything.

They walk along the path. It's straight, following the irrigation ditch that stretches for miles into the distance. It feels infinite, this path. They come to a display board that shows the birds that can be spotted on the marshes. She squints and shields her eyes from the sun, but there are no birds. Nothing in the sky. The grasses shimmer and ripple. The Man joins her at her side.

There is a reconstruction of the Neolithic trackway not too far from here.

A what?

I told you about it in the car, perhaps you don't remember. The Neolithic inhabitants of the marsh built a trackway, more than 5000 years ago. There's a replica here that goes out a little way across the peat bog. We can walk along it if you like.

Where does it go?

I'm not sure. Would you like to go and find out?

They continue on, side by side. The Man ducks under a tree, helping her under too. She can feel the wine, acidic and yellow in her body, rocking her from side to side. Her vision flickers and then steadies. He takes her hand and helps her onto the first of the planks that forms the trackway. The planks snake ahead of them, through the reeds and shrubs. Angled wooden struts on either side suspend the track two or three feet above the soft, waterlogged ground. The planks are just wide enough for a person to stand with their feet together. She wonders about asking the man if he can tell her how big people's feet were in the Neolithic era, but the thought fizzes and floats away before she can open her mouth. Her brain simmers in the heat, all of its ideas bristling near the surface. The Man is ahead of her, striding along the trackway that juts out across the marsh. His footsteps make no sound.

*

Flora is adding up the remaining hours of her visit to her family home. She had heard the garage door clunk shut. Felt it rather than heard it. You get used to the sounds and sighs of a house, especially the one you grew up in. It becomes like an extension of your body; of all that you've ever known. Even after just one term away from home she feels like she has slotted easily back into this house and its slow, smothering rhythms. It's like putting on a pair of old shoes. Comforting and disappointing all at once. Nothing ever happens here. She looks at the screen in her palm, turns on her notifications, sees there are none. Turns them off again. She thinks about sending a message to Lou, composes it in her head, thinks about typing it out, but just in Notes, so that Lou won't see her typing. She thinks of things like: *My family are awful* or *Greetings from the hellscape of my family home* or *Hey*

how's it going, what time are you back after the break? Lou
hadn't replied to her last message though, and that was only
last night, so it would look weird to get in touch again so
soon. Flora doesn't want Lou to think she's needy; she wants
Lou to think she's weird and cool and eccentric and funny.
Flora is all of these things, as most people know, but she
can't see it yet. Lou can't see it either.

*

It's dark, and Milo is in the forest, but everything is easy.
He's feeling really good; really boosted. There are a lot of
enemies, but he knocks them all out of the way superfast.
There's an old woman in a tree somewhere around here that
he needs to talk to. Milo runs up to her, his feet crunching
and cold in the snow. It smells like trees here; it's really
cool. His armour glitters. There's wet in the air. He pivots up
and sees that there's sleet. He pulls his hood over his head.
Milo swings his head from side to side, it's harder with the
advanced armour but he's still really energised so his legs
swing about quickly and easily. On a leftward head swing
he sees an old woman in a hollow of a tree. She's tiny but
expands rapidly when he sees her. He jogs over, crunch-
crunch-crunch through the snow. The woman's fire is jade
green. That means something, but Milo can't remember
what now. She says, *your old father has the right time*.
Milo asks her again, but she just says the same thing. He

tries again but she doesn't say anything. Milo looks around, swinging left to right again. It's quiet now. No enemies. Just the zappy crackle of the old woman's fire. Milo checks the Friend Stream to see if anyone else is here but it's empty. He wishes, for the thousandth time, that his parents would let him connect to the global network, but he's not allowed until he turns twelve. Eight more months. He crosses off the days on his calendar every morning, scratching with a red pen.

Milo's thirsty. He reaches around on the floor for the orange drink that he snuck up here when it all got weird at lunchtime. He pauses the forest and it washes to a frozen grey. His bedroom comes into focus around him; soft silence. His bed, his Lego, his army men, his schoolbag. A picture of them all on his bedside table, the five of them. The picture was taken a few years ago—on that trip to the marshes—so they all look the same but not the same. Milo remembers the rustling noise as the wind bothered at the tall grasses. It was before Flora shaved her head and before Rae stopped talking. A cold, bright day.

Taller than you, buddy, his father had said.

Milo hadn't liked that idea. The pale stems that reached towards the clouds that hurried away overhead. He didn't like the noise, like whispers, like the land was too alive; too clever. He remembers pulling at one of the stems at the side of the path. It was rooted tightly and didn't come away in his hand, instead leaving a pink line down the centre of his palm. Milo remembers hearing a noise like a dinosaur;

a long, low booming sound coming from underneath them; from the earth. He remembers how his father stopped, like he'd been paused. The look on his father's face was like he'd won something. He explained that it was this type of strange bird; one that sat low in the reed beds and was very hard to spot. He explained that this bird had been extinct and then not extinct, so in fact it *was* kind of like a dinosaur.

Doesn't it sound amazing, Milo, his father said.

Milo recalls his father in that moment; as open and bright as the marsh, excited about this newly un-extinct bird. He recalls his siblings, somewhere, dragging their feet. He recalls looking for his mother, finding her in the middle distance looking away from them, too far away to hear about the dinosaur-bird.

Milo's mind wanders back to lunchtime just gone, his mother's face clouding over. Like when he pauses the forest, a quiet grey that suspends everything. He listens out for his parents, hears his father typing—clackity-clackity-click-clack—in the next room.

*

Rae floats on her back; eyes closed. The water is warm and clear. The sand at the bottom is creamy-white. There are no fish, but that's good. Rae doesn't like it when there are fish, but doesn't mind a bit of seaweed, or some smooth rocks. But no fish, no crabs, no jellyfish or any other soft and dangerous wobbly things. Her eyes open slightly. The sun shimmers on the water. It's amazing how easily you float here. Hardly any wind, tiny rippling waves. On the beach, far away, are the shapes of Phyllis and Roy88 in their swimsuits, but they're playing a game by the looks of things, and Rae doesn't feel like doing that right now. Phyllis has a huge crush on Roy88 anyway, and Rae doesn't want to sit there while they throw insults at each other over her head. Rae tries to meditate but it doesn't work. However hard she tries to hold it down, her squirming mind wrestles itself free, scurrying back towards that moment at lunch. Milo going on and on again about being allowed to connect to the global network, saying he had friends he needed to speak to; that it wasn't fair. Their mother saying that no one needed to speak to their friends all the time. Milo saying that *she* did, and *Dad* did, so it was *doubly unfair.* Rae recalls their mother's mouth twitching like a bird on a wire. Her face blank, just for a moment; her father looking straight down at his food.

I am an adult, her mother had said as her face sprang back into life, *and the people I speak to are work people.*

Yeah, but they're all still your friends. You've got loads of work friends. And Dad speaks to his friend from work all the time.

Something had changed then, but Rae knows it's something she's a long way away from understanding.

The water tingles as it caresses Rae's skin. She likes this swimsuit but might change it soon. She's seen a few people on the beach in the same one.

124

*

Chaffinches are monogamous. Pair bonds last from one breeding season to the next. There are four clutches of eggs—not yet hatched—in the nest boxes. James checks each one in turn. There are three more mating pairs in the other boxes. He pushes some codes into different cells on the spreadsheet. He keeps the nest-box live-feeds pinned to his home screen at all times. The birds shift themselves, settling down over the clutches of eggs. Those still without eggs dart in and out of the boxes, on and off camera, on and off his screen. James thinks about the distance birds travel, the way they return to the same pair bond, the efficiency of it, the inevitability of it.

Angeline is typing...

Four and five look like they're almost ready. Is it 12 days now?

Yeah, looks like it! Bets as to who's first? My money's on four!

Oh, I do believe that's quite unethical, James.

He looks at the words—his name—typed out by Angeline. He imagines her slender hands as they write to him. He thinks about the trip to Varanger last summer. He thinks about it a lot. He thinks about what Milo had said at lunchtime. It hadn't been that bad, had it? No. Milo didn't know anything. Besides, how would Milo possibly know about Angeline? James had been very careful. That's what they had agreed.

Nothing had been said, not overtly. Everything was encoded, loaded with meaning so elaborate that only James and Angeline would understand. What had happened on that trip had happened in person. It was a live trip; untraceable, their fieldwork highly classified. Only really evidenced by data. James leans back in his chair, remembering the smell of the pine in the damp forest, steaming slightly in the morning sunshine. His fingers combing through the ends of Angeline's hair, wet from the rain shower. Her skin. Her eyes — hazel, reflecting the forest in miniature — glistening and alive. Her voice rippling through the whoosh of the wind in the trees.

Maybe Milo *had* sensed something. Kids pick up on this stuff. But there was nothing that could be proven. This would all be forgotten about soon. James thought about his wife, who would be downstairs now, finishing the wine. No doubt on her laptop.

Angeline waves to James and goes offline. He deletes the messages like they'd agreed. The spreadsheet's cells are full. James hears Milo whooping and grunting along with his game in the next room. Silence where his daughters should be. He doesn't want to go downstairs yet. He looks around the study for some other Sunday afternoon preoccupation to make itself known to him. A person can find all sorts of things around the home to distract them from their thoughts.

I know, he thinks, and opens the software for the Man. You have to power it up and sync it with the home devices before you can use it. The programme opens, scans James's face. The home screen shows an image of the Man they bought yesterday. The image walks into the centre and stands waiting, its chest moving up and down slightly as if breathing. The screen invites James to power up the Man and sync him with the device. James taps. Taps again.

Man Out of Range.

Makes no sense, it's only downstairs, still in the garage; still in its packaging. He listens. Silence where his daughters should be. Silence, still, where his wife should be. Maybe she's taken the dog out.

*

The woman and Man come to the end of the trackway. A wooden viewing platform extends out across the marsh. No one is there. The marsh teems with life. The woman can feel it bubbling and rustling beneath the surface. She crouches down on the platform, then eases herself down and stretches out flat on her back. The wooden slats have soaked up the sun; it feels nice to be perfectly straight and for her bones to align against the warm wood. The feeling is almost painful, but not quite. The Man sits down beside her, cross-legged.

Tell me about this place. But tell me quietly.

Once this was all underwater. There were nomadic communities that would build settlements on the ground, high enough to rise out of the marshes. There are still places near here that have 'isle' in their name. The nomads would travel between islands along trackways like these, or in simple canoes. The reed beds were richly fertile, and therefore ideal for grazing livestock or hunting for game—

Was it better then, do you think?

I don't know. Are you asking me to make a judgement?

Yes.

If I consider this question carefully, I'd say that there are trade-offs. Ancient communities like those during the Neolithic era had different concerns. They most likely would have lived from day to day, hour to hour in some cases. They would have been motivated by instincts in the same way that you are, I imagine. Hunger, thirst, fear, fatigue, lust. The need for closeness with others, the need to laugh, the need to cry. Care for their offspring; care for their partners.

So just like now then, only simpler.

Many people now would consider that to be a simpler way of life, yes. But death would have been around the corner all the time. Moreover, so much of the world was unknown. They would have been full of fear. Perhaps this wasn't such a pleasant state to be in.

I guess we'll never know.

Correct. There isn't a way of knowing.

The woman sits up, finishes the wine, shields her eyes as she looks out over the marsh to where the small dome of an island rises in the middle distance.

Funny, she says, *we've lived out here for ages, must have been here hundreds of times, but I've never noticed that island before.*

∗

It's gone. And the car's gone. What the fuck was she thinking? This is like drink driving. She must have had three, maybe four glasses at lunchtime. If she crashes, that's one thing, but the Man isn't even registered to us and—fuck—we haven't even made a single payment on it yet. I haven't even activated the insurance on it. Why the fuck would she do this?

James yells, louder than he intends, to Flora and Rae. They slope down and assemble in the doorway that connects the house to the garage. No one heard her leave. Flora says she thought she heard the door clunk. She uses a tiny voice. James tries to soften his features. Milo appears in between his siblings, his oval face flushed and rigid as it adjusts from being away from the blue light of his console.

Your mother has gone off in the car with the new Man, he says.

Oh, says Flora. Rae says nothing but turns as if to go back into the house. The others turn too, as if to follow.

No, James says, *no, we have to go and look for her. Now.*

Well, I'm not, says Flora. Rae says nothing. Rae hasn't said anything for nearly 18 months. James looks at his middle child—a pale and thin creature with pale and thin hair—and feels a surge of something. Anger? Despair? Despair. It goes, again, swallowed by a wave of irritation. James looks at the three of them; different-sized simulations of him. Fresher faces, tighter skin.

Why has she gone off and not told us? asks Milo.

Probably just went to the hypermarket or something, Flora says, looking down at her device. *Oh look, no. The tracker says she's at the marshes. Maybe she took the dog—*

But the dog bustles in, her feet skittering on the concrete floor, weaving between the children and James with all the energy of an unwalked animal.

In the end they get into James's car. He drives with one hand, his phone in the other with the tracker. It's still there, at the marshes. Flora and Rae each turn their heads to look out of their windows. Milo sits in the centre, face fixed ahead, pale now too, like his sisters.

*

The woman and the Man sit side by side on the viewing platform. The reed bed flickers all around them. Pale plants crane towards the light; dark, spongy mosses sprawl across the ground, breaking off here and there but always reconnecting. Bulrushes and ferns curl and stretch, all reaching up towards the sky. The water rises up too, joining with the land, emerging out of the earth. The sun washes everything in gold, all of it glistening and alive.

Did you find anything? she asks him.

No, he says. *Nothing.*

So, you don't know everything, she says, nudging him.

No, I don't. I told you that already.

The woman stands up and stretches. She squints into the distance to get a better look at the island. The light makes it look unreal, gilding its surface. It can't be more than a couple of miles from here. How could she not have noticed it before?

We should go over there, she says, *check it out.*

A splashing. A dog in the water. The woman turns and the Man stands up and turns with her. She sees her husband, striding along the footpath. Her husband and all of her children and her dog, trying to launch itself into the reed bed. All of them confused and irritated in the heat of the day. She feels something burning in her chest, something like fear, something like rising anger.

What are you doing? her husband shouts. His voice sounds high-pitched and nasal. *We've only just got it. It's not insured properly. It's not registered.*

She stands up and faces her husband. The Man stands there perfectly still, just behind her. She doesn't reply.

What—what are you doing? he says it again. James is frightened, she realises. She doesn't know if she's ever seen him frightened before.

It's dangerous, James shouts. Milo is next to him. The girls behind. She can't make out the expressions on their faces. She looks down, realises—for the first time—that she's not wearing any shoes. Her feet are burnished ochre with dirt.

Mum, what are you doing? Milo looks older, suddenly. Older but smaller. Shrunken and far away.

Who is that? the Man asks. *Who are they?*

It occurs to the woman that the Man has never seen James before. It occurs to her that he has never seen anyone before, other than her. The children. The children. None of them look like her. She has always known this. Maybe there's something slowing down in her, something to do with age. But there were these moments—these glitches—if she looked in the mirror next to her children, where they look like soft, gelatinous strangers. She remembers when her children were babies, their three little skulls, each stretched with a thin, pale membrane. She remembered how awful that had made her feel; those little skeins of vulnerability that she had been forced to look at every day until their hair grew and she could forget about it. She remembers these feelings, but she can't remember her children's births. She thinks then that she should probably remember their births, but that thought flits away too.

James is scrolling frantically at the screen in his hand. He's shouting something, yelling commands. The children have gone. The children are back in the car. She can't remember what the children look like anymore, suddenly. She can't feel

132

them. She realises she doesn't care. All of those thoughts are undulating now—spinning faster and faster, but away from her slightly—outside of her.

She feels the hard, smooth surface of the Man's palm as he takes hers, and they step off the platform together. Her feet sink into the ground. The ground is viscous; unstable. It's black like tar underneath the tufts of grass. If she could just get out of range of James; if they both could. She looks at the Man and he nods. She realises that no one knows her better than he does. They start out through the peat bog, away from James' voice, towards the island that rises out of the mist like a temple.

The Unreliable Nature Writer Stands At The Bar Before The First Dance

– Oh, hello again.

Did you find your wife?

– Yes, she needed help with the kids; it's a long day for them. Do you have any?

Any wives?

– Kids.

No.

– Ah, very wise!

Why do you say that?

– Oh, no, I mean, it was just a joke. They're um...they're great.

Can I get you a drink?

– Oh no, no. I'm alright for now.

So, what do you do?

– Oh, I work in AI. Artificial Intelligence.

Are you a designer?

– No, no I'm on the sales side of things. The business end, as it were.

The money end.

– Yes, the boring bit. Actually, I will have another drink.

Sure. But is it boring?

– Thanks, yes. Gin and tonic. Sorry, what did you say?

Is it boring? Your job in AI.

– Um, *is it boring*? Well, the company itself is really dynamic and interesting. We were a small start-up that now employs over a thousand people globally, we've got some of the best people working for us, we're developing designs that will hopefully make everyone's lives easier but, yes, the day-to-day is pretty, um, yeah, pretty mundane, I suppose.

Yes. Do you create surveillance software?

– What? Um, no. not strictly speaking anyway.

You either do or you don't.

– Well, some of the stuff we develop could *technically* be used to surveille people. But we're an ethical company; our CEO has great credentials. This is what people don't really understand; a lot of these guys do have their heart in the right place. We're not all evil geniuses looking to take over the world, no matter what you might think.

I don't think you're a genius.

– Sorry? Noisy in here—

I said: I don't think you're an evil genius.

– No, no. I know. But I suppose I get a bit defensive of what I do. I know there are some nefarious people out there, but there are a lot of good guys too.

You're a good guy?

– Haha—well that's up to you to decide isn't it.

Not if you believe in moral absolutes.

– Do you?

I haven't decided yet.

– Ah, yes of course, that would make sense for the Unreliable Nature Writer, wouldn't it! Are you always this evasive? I don't think I've ever met—

I think that's your wife over there.

– Where? Oh yes. She's fine. Catching up with old friends. To be honest it's quite nice just to be able to be ourselves again, not having to focus on the kids the whole time.

Didn't you just say she needed help with the kids?

– No, no she prefers it if I don't interfere. I just get in the way—haha—where was I?

You were explaining how you're a good guy.

– Oh, I was, was I? Well, I don't know about that. It sounds to me like you have a bit of a problem with tech guys.

Tech guys?

– Yeah. Guys in tech. You're a bit suspicious of them, I reckon.

Why would that be the case, do you think?

– Well, you probably think that white, straight, reasonably affluent men who are approaching middle age shouldn't be trusted with unprecedented technology. You probably think that it's dangerous in our hands.

Do you think you're dangerous?

– Haha—who knows? Maybe I am. What do you think?

You could be.

– Do I seem dangerous?

Not especially, no. But then I guess statistically you're more of a danger to your wife than you are to me.

– Oh. What? I'm not sure I—

Women are more likely to be—

– Oh. This isn't what I —

You asked if I thought you were dangerous.

– I suppose I wasn't expecting you to get onto, um, murder? quite so quickl —

You prefer to build up to that.

– Um, I don't know how we got onto —

Don't be so hard on yourself. I'm sure you're not going to murder your wife.

– No, obviously not. What a thing to suggest.

It's just an uncomfortable statistic.

– Yes, a bit uncomfortable but it's fine, I can take a joke!

Are you alright?

– Why does it feel like everything is a constant battle? It feels like there are all these hoops to jump through nowadays.

You must feel exhausted.

– It *is* exhausting, yes. *Thank* you.

Does it feel like you're clinging on with your fingernails, trying to claw your way back up the cliff edge?

– Well—a bit, yes.

Do your fingers hurt?

– I'm not sure I—

Shall we do some shots? Let's do some shots, I'll get them.

– What?

Shots! Whatever you want.

– OK, go on then.

You sure?

– One won't hurt. Oh *two*, yes sure, OK, fine—

Your fingers will feel better. Well, numb anyway.

– OK, if you say so! God, that's very strong, isn't it? Look, I'm trying my best. That's all I can do, right—God, that really is *very* strong—What else can I do?

You could dismantle everything.

– Oh OK, and how would I do that?

You can probably work that one out for yourself. You seem like a smart guy.

– God, Jesus Christ, what was in those? They were actually rather nice, but this aftertaste—tastes like—

Grass.

– Yes! Grass! And terribly strong. The lights are kind of spinning—no! not spinning, sort of jittering—is that happening for you, or is it just me?

I think it's just you.

– It's great though, really energising! What do they put in these? Grass probably, haha! Another? Great. Oh...This is embarrassing, I don't seem to have my wallet—

Don't worry, I'll get these.

– No, no, I insist. This is very embarrassing. Oh god. I'm not very good on spirits. I'm sure I had it though. Maybe I can charge them to the room, or maybe my wife—

Are you alright? You're swaying quite a lot.

– I'm great! Never better. These are actually delicious, once you get used to that grassy taste. And something else, something like—

Earth.

– Yes! Anyway, look, I *can* do something to dismantle it all, I'm sure. I'm sure. I'll work it out. I will. For you. For everyone, I mean. I want to do better.

That's great. Mind those empties with your elbow there. I think you've spilled quite a lot of that one. Don't—oh, no, don't worry they're bringing a dustpan and brush. Are you sure you don't want to go to the dancefloor before it all starts? It seems she's looking over at you.

– Yes, no. Sorry, I've made quite a mess there. No, I don't need to go over. It's fine, she'll be fine.

They're so beautiful, aren't they?

– Who are?

Those two; the newlyweds.

– They're both great. Do you know, I've never known a nicer couple. It's so invigorating to see two people so in love. They look so happy. Wait, hold on, didn't you say beauty was pretty pointless or something earlier?

I don't think I said that, did I?

Re: Wreck Event

[Please find attached notes on your version of the event that occurred last winter. Whilst I am willing to accept that we see things differently, and that we've come to separate viewpoints after some time apart, there are certain assertions from you that I am not prepared to accept. I'm sure we can meet in the middle, but currently the version you have offered is riddled with omissions and falsehoods that cause me to feel extremely uncomfortable. I will seek to rectify these as best I can. I hope you are well. I hope you are keeping warm. I hope things are improving for you.]

The morning you left was the morning we woke up to the dead birds. I waited upstairs so that you could get ready alone; so that you could leave in the way you wanted.[1] We had said all that needed to be said. The door clicked shut, but then, minutes later, you were back. You said you couldn't get your van down the lane because it was covered in birds.[2] They were dead or dying, you said. You had one in your hand, its little head poking through the gap between your index finger and thumb. You held it out, as proof.[3]

---

1 There is an implication here that I was the person who chose to leave. This is incorrect. You compelled me to leave. Please edit the text to reflect this.

2 This is not what I said.

3 This is not what I did.

It's OK, I said. *I believe you.*

You opened your gloved hand anyway, revealing the entirety of the wilted thing inside. It was small and black. A starling or a blackbird.[4]

I turned my head and looked out of the window so that I wouldn't have to look at it, and you walked back outside, taking it with you. You put the bird down, carefully, onto the garden wall. You lowered it so gently, like it was a sleeping baby, and it lay there on top of the brickwork.

I can't get my van out because of the birds. You said it again when you came back in; like you couldn't quite believe it was true.[5]

I came out of the house in my pyjamas and wellingtons[6] to have a look; to see for myself. The track gave way to the lane, if you'll recall, and it was frozen solid. I couldn't see what you were talking about, but I felt the terrain shift under by boots and there on the ground spaced out at regular intervals were hundreds of dead birds.[7] The sun was still low in the

---

4 It was a gull. I was holding it in both hands.

5 This makes me sound like a ditherer. I am not a ditherer. I knew what was happening and why.

6 You were in your clothes from the night before, that you had slept in. The black dress you'd passed out in. You had lipstick smeared across your face.

7 There were approximately twenty or so birds, all seabirds. All adults, no juveniles.

sky, and we followed the lane together. Stepping gingerly between the birds as they lay on ground, all very still all separated out as though someone had visited in the night and laid each one down, very precisely.

You said some of them were still alive, I said.

No, I didn't.

You did, you said 'dead or dying'.

Maybe I thought some were still alive.

They're not though, are they.

No.

We walked out onto the main road. I had tried to count the birds in the lane, got confused after about eighty. As we rounded the corner we were met with more still, spread neatly across the tarmac.

Hundreds of them, you said.

I wondered aloud why the birds hadn't been run over. It's quiet up here at this time of year, but there is usually a delivery van or a care-worker on an early shift.[8]

---

8 You were drunk, still, from the night before. Babbling, incoherent. You 'wondered' many things aloud, none of them especially logical.

They were probably completely freaked out at the sight of them, you said.[9]

I thought about how easily a set of tires could plough through the limp little bodies. There would be track marks of dark blood, a paste of guts and bones, beaks and feathers. It wouldn't matter to the birds though. They were already dead.[10]

We stood on the stretch of the main road that looks out over the bay. The tide was out, lurking somewhere. Low tide exposed the grim, lumpen rocks that were strewn across the beach. Beaches are menacing in the winter, you always said. Sharp, cold edges and dull, thick sand.

You shielded your eyes from the sun with a gloved hand. You hated the way the sunlight bounced off the wet road in the wintertime here.[11] You hated the cold.[12] You hated the land; the language. You hated that I liked those things so much.[13] You tried, though, I'll give you that, but the land seemed to hate you just as much. The wind picked up, and I thought I glimpsed tears working their way out of the

---

9   Inaccurate.

10   Inaccurate. Many of the gulls were still alive, some were hopping about, others batting their wings against the tarmac. This was arguably more distressing than what you have rendered here, albeit less poetic.

11   Inaccurate.

12   Inaccurate. Where I live now is far colder, as you know.

13   Inaccurate. Misleading. Spiteful, even.

corners of your eyes. How often do you cry these days? Is it any better now?[14]

A white van appeared, and you ran towards it, waving your arms as if you were guiding in a plane. The van slowed to a halt and the driver stuck his head out of the window. He was young and fresh-faced, with a knitted fisherman's hat.

Alright? he said. *What's all this?*

It's birds, you said. *A load of dead birds.*

The man got out. He was wearing paint-stained overalls that were far too big for him. He walked towards us, rolling up his sleeves to reveal forearms covered with tattoos. The man crouched down next to where the spread of birds started, reached over and poked one.

Weird, man. He stood up. *How'd they die?*[15]

I don't know, you said. *We woke up and found them like this. We—she lives down there.*

The man pulled a pouch of tobacco from his pocket and started rolling a cigarette.[16]

---

14 …

15 This is largely commensurate with how I remember the conversation.

16 He was smoking Marlboro Reds.

You on holiday? he said. You rolled your eyes.[17]

No. She lives down there.

You probably want to phone someone, don't you? he said. *Get these moved out the way.*[18]

Yeah, you said. *I just wanted to get my van out of the lane, actually. I need to get going.*

Thin, fraying clouds hurried overhead, sending shadows across the bay. The tide was starting to come in, seeping back over the rocks and the dark sand. I thought about what it would be like to go and walk along the beach on my own. I thought about how it would feel to be going back to the house alone.[19]

When I looked back, you and the man were huddled together, hunched over your phones. He told us his name was Gareth. He found you the number for the animal warden and you spoke to someone on the phone.[20] Two cars

---

17 I don't recall doing this.

18 I find it risible that you would remember his words and actions with such clarity yet 'forget' mine so readily.

19 You were laughing and joking, smoking his cigarettes, whispering in his ear. It was extremely awkward.

20 He tried to give you the number, but you dropped your phone onto the ground, and it smashed. One of the least injured gulls hopped over and started to peck at the shards of plastic and tempered glass.

stopped behind Gareth's van. A horn sounded, then another, so Gareth went over to talk to the drivers.[21] Both of them craned their necks out of their windows, but neither got out. It was too cold, I suppose. After a couple of minutes, the cars each reversed and left. Perhaps the sight of hundreds of dead birds—wet and dull and spread across the road—was too awful to contemplate.[22]

Gareth got back in his van to keep warm. I could see him through the windscreen talking to someone on his phone; laughing, flicking ash from his rollup out of the window.[23] The birds lay there, damp and still. You trudged down to where the bodies petered out at the opposite end, just in case anyone came from the other direction. I watched you, guarding them, with your arms folded, squinting into the brightening morning.[24] I still think of you when the mornings are cold like that, when everything glistens too intensely.

---

21 Gareth walked over to the first driver and slapped the roof of their car. The driver rolled down the window and told Gareth to move aside, after which he swore excessively at the driver (a woman in her mid-60s as I recall) who got out of the car and jabbed a pointed finger in his face, before getting back in and performing an aggressive U-turn while Gareth attempted to chase after her.

22 This is the sort of hyperbole that does not serve either of us. It's this poetic exaggeration that makes it difficult to be with you for lengths of time.

23 You got in with him. You had him turn on the radio. I could see you through the windscreen rifling through the things on the front seat and footwell. You put on his jacket, let him light your cigarette.

24 I attempted to resuscitate several of the birds. I removed my coat, my scarf and my jumper. I wrapped a number of them up to keep warm and moved them out of the road.

Eventually we saw a blue van trundle through the valley from the other direction. It stopped just short of where you stood, watching over the birds. The van door opened, and a figure heaved itself out of the drivers' side, dressed head to toe in a silvery-white boiler suit. It had a vented mask over its face. You went over; I saw you gesture to the birds. I could tell by its gait that the figure was that of a woman.[25]

I was too far away to hear what you were saying, but I watched as you helped her pick up one of the bodies, held your hands near to hers as she turned it over and pressed gently on its little chest. It was like you didn't want to believe that the thing was really dead.[26] I could feel that you wanted it to spring back to life and flutter off, darting away into the trees that cling to the cliffs.

Instead, she handed it to you. Then she went to her van and brought out a stack of plastic crates filled with wide reams of cotton wool. You beckoned me over.

This is—what was it? Becky?—Yeah. Becky's got to take the birds off to be looked at in a lab, you said. You didn't tell Becky my name.[27]

---

25 Becky is someone I know very well, as do you. It feels unreasonable not to allude to this here.

26 In a way. Yes. This is true.

27 I didn't need to, Becky already knows your name. You've been to her house for supper several times.

What do you think might have happened? I asked her. She took off her mask to talk to me. Her teeth were crooked at the front.[28]

It's hard to say, she said. She stopped, resting the crate she was carrying on her hip, and looked at the bodies, all laid out on the tarmac. *I mean, I've seen individual birds that crash land into patios, or windows, but nothing on this scale before.*[29]

We stood together, the three of us, and looked at the road. Some of the birds were on their backs, feet curled as if still clutching a branch or a telephone wire. Others were on their sides, wings tucked in, beaks pressed into their chests. It was like they had all gone to sleep.

We'll give you a hand, shall we? I said.[30]

I should really ask you to leave it to me, Becky said, *but there are so many, and it looks like it'll rain soon.* She smiled and handed me a set of surgical gloves and one of the plastic crates. Up close I could see thick red

---

28 Inaccurate. Becky has lovely, straight teeth.

29 *I* said this. This is what *I* said. Not Becky.

30 You said this, rather aggressively, as you picked up one of the crates and started scraping the dead birds off the road. There weren't many, but you kept dropping them. Becky tried to help you and you shouted, 'BACK OFF' and snatched back the crate.

hair that was greying at the temples, escaping from the hood of her protective suit. She smelled very faintly of antiseptic. *Plus,* she went on, *your partner has already handled some of them.*[31]

We both winced at the word, but Becky didn't notice. We set about picking up the birds, each of them cold, each of them definitely dead.

Gareth got out of his van and sauntered over.

I'll help as well, shall I? He didn't wait for an answer.

The four of us began collecting up the bodies, following Becky's lead. We carefully scooped up the dead birds and placed them in layers in the plastic crates in between the swathes of cotton wool. Each bird felt stiff, but there was resistance when I picked some of them up, like there was still some remnant of life in them. We cleared the birds in silence, even though I wanted to ask Becky what she was going to do next, and what would happen to the birds in the lab. It took an hour to clear the road. Then Gareth said he would come with us to help pick up the birds in the lane.

---

31 This is entirely fictional. She knows me by name, of course, and she pointed out *helpfully* that what I had done, in handling the birds that were still alive, was the correct course of action.

Haven't you got somewhere to be? you asked him. I wondered why he annoyed you so much. Then I remembered that everyone annoys you, especially here.[32]

I like your tattoos, I said—quickly—before Gareth could answer you. You were standing behind me, out of sight, when I said it. But I know you heard.[33]

Ah, thanks, man, he said, and started telling me all about them as we set about clearing the lane. There was a rat with glowing red eyes across the inside of his left forearm, inspired by a song he liked. There was a giant squid, splaying its tentacles across one hand, wrapping in and out of his fingers.[34]

That one was for my grandad, he said, rotating his hand so that I could see where the tattooist had etched the mottled skin of the squid across Gareth's thin, pale knuckles. *He was a sailor. He died last year. I wanted something to remember him by.*

By now we were nearly back at the house, and almost all the birds were put away neatly in the boxes. Gareth told me

---

32 This is accurate.

33 This is accurate. I knew what you were doing.

34 Gareth, with your help, stripped down to his vest, and with great pleasure it seemed, was describing in detail the tattoos across not only his forearms, but his chest, stomach and legs too. You felt it necessary to touch each one. Becky and I continued with the birds, and then, once finished, sat in her van to keep warm while this was taking place.

about the final tattoo. On his left arm, near the veins on the inside of his wrist, was a blackbird with a yellow beak, open in song. Underneath was a scroll, bearing tiny letters that spelled out 'Aderyn Du'.

That says 'blackbird', he said. *Did you know that?*

No, I said. *I'd never heard that word before.*[35]

That one's for my girlfriend. She sings really beautifully. As he spoke, Gareth picked up the very last dead bird. It was the one that you had laid gently on the garden wall earlier that morning. He held it tenderly next to the tattoo on his arm. It didn't look anything like the tattoo. I felt like crying.

Weird that I've got that one though, isn't it? he said.[36]

No one replied.

Feels like an omen or something, Gareth said, quietly. He brought the bird up close to his face then stroked the top of its head with one pale finger, very softly.[37]

---

35 This is the only accurate part of your recollection of this exchange.

36 Nothing about this was weird. It was all so incredibly predictable.

37 Gareth stroked your face with his hand. He ran his fingers through your hair. He didn't touch any of the birds.

You were staring at me. Was that the last thing you wanted to remember of this place? Me, standing in the cold in my pyjamas,[38] with two locals and all of these dead birds.

Gareth lowered the last bird into the box with the others, and Becky closed the lid, pressing down the four corners to secure it. It was the same sort of plastic storage crate that we used when we moved here. I remembered, then, about the boxes and bags in the back of your van that were full of your clothes and books and records; the kitchenware you had insisted was yours; the coffee machine I was too exhausted to fight over. All of those things, those objects, waiting in there for you to take them away from this place.[39] The four of us stood there for a moment, looking at the five crates on the ground that were packed with the corpses of the birds. It began to rain.

Shit, I've got to go, Gareth said. We all stood there for a moment. He waved a hand in the air as he walked off, back towards his van.

Becky left too. We watched as she disappeared around the bend in the lane. Then it was just us. I asked if you wanted to come in and have a cup of tea before you left. It felt like the right thing to do. But you said no. You had to get on if

---

38   Dress from the previous night, face smeared with makeup.

39   I had no choice. I had to leave. It was impossible not to.

156

you were going to get back before dark. It was a long drive, after all.[40]

What do you think they'll do with all those birds? I said.

I felt like I needed to stall for time; I'm not sure why.

They'll do a post-mortem on them, I guess. You opened the door of your van and climbed in. *Find out what went wrong.*

---

40   It was, yes. The drive was very, very long.

The Bioindicator

The side effects are minimal. There are ten in the packet. It's perfectly safe. Really is the best way.

The pharmacist hands them over in an unmarked bag, whispers that he takes them with no worrying consequences. His skin's luminous; undeniably beautiful. He smiles and says, *it's my last day.*

I take the first tablet on the walk back. It's still early. It tastes of lychees. Back in the house, I get very close to the mirror by the front door. There are visible pores on my nose. How do you get rid of those? The taste of lychees is still there at the sides of my tongue. Max is calling; I mute him. I look at the skin on my arms, the small hairs. Completely normal. Anaïs is calling; I mute her.

I boiled it down ages ago. It's about clarity. When we strip everything else away, this is what we are left with. A desire for clarity. There are other problems in my life, sure, but I don't need to worry about those now.

The side effects are minimal in comparison to the benefits. I've used it for weeks and the results are there already. Don't read too much about the side effects!

The hallway of this house is too dark. The walls are damp. Mould blooms flamboyantly across a ceiling-bulge. Water collects. Drips. I'm the only one here. In the hallway mirror, an outline creeps from the hemline of my shorts, and the shape of a thinner leg appears under the skin of my own.

I haven't experienced anything bad at all, but we all have different body-types. You've got to be careful, but nothing is risk-free these days!

This was my parents' house. We were meant to be renovating it, but it's too late. Max is trying to call. Anaïs is trying to call. I touch the skin of my leg, where the shadow of the other leg becomes more defined. No longer a shadow, more of a shape. Or maybe it's just the light. I turn to the other side, but my right leg is normal. The pores on my nose are widening, darkening. I haven't slept properly in weeks.

The playroom, as it was, is stacked high with removal boxes. The ceiling leaks here too. The cardboard covering the holes swells, dries out, swells again. Some of the boxes have my name on them, some have Max's name. The window has a crack in it. A bird has made a nest in the window box. A grey wagtail, Max said when he was here last. The nest is empty.

Great decision, best I ever made! Go for it! Get plenty of sleep! That's the best thing for skin!

Downstairs is cooler than upstairs. The kitchen table is covered in used cosmetics. Cleansing wipes, mascara tubes, cream blusher, retinol, hyaluronic acid, hair masque sachets. All mine. I find a rubbish bag under the sink and—with a wide arm—sweep everything inside. I run the tap, fill a glass, swallow two more of the tablets and put my cheek on the clean surface of the kitchen table.

A dream opens up in the centre of the kitchen floor, the decades-old linoleum peels back and a dark pool deepens. My parents are down there. I remember a pond, a pool, a monochrome day in autumn. My father's face, howling and invisible in the nest of his fingers. Other people—party guests, or doctors—smoking, pacing. It could have been a bad day or a good day. His days were always one or the other, ours too. Max is calling. The leg under my skin throbs, then shudders free, tipping me sideways. My parents are muted by the water. Something drips. Their faces tremble. It's hard to tell if they're laughing or crying.

Absolutely fantastic results! Best thing I ever did for my skin!

I wake to the sound of knocking. I swallow the fourth tablet on my way to the door, peer through the spyhole. The worried moon of Max's face peers back. I creep away and sit back down at the kitchen table. The tap drips. The clock is still ticking. The sounds step in and out of time with one another; a heart murmur. I remember running out of the back door of this house, and down to the end of the garden. Running so fast that my chest felt like it would crack open. I remember sitting with my legs stretched out before me in the long grass, a caterpillar ploughing through the hairs that stood up on my shin. When I return to the door, Max is gone. I sit down again. My hips hurt. My side stretches away, muscular. Sexy. When I look down, I see contours, silt beds, marshes fizzing with life. My left leg is redundant now, my new leg stronger. The right one hasn't appeared yet, but something buzzes at my neck. A frill. I crawl over to the sink where I left the packet. I pop the last four tablets from the blister pack.

Lay them out ready for the later stages. In a pill organiser if you have one, or on a large plate.

The outline of the right leg appears. With it, an unbearable urge to clean. The frill at my neck lengthens and shortens with the temperature, so I open the windows and draw the curtains. The kitchen glistens as my new right leg slides out from under the skin. I think of a soft-bodied thing—piercing an egg case that quivers on a leaf—shaking itself free. I balance by the sink, shifting the weight between my two new legs. Two more tablets. I take one, pocket the other.

My parents moved here and renovated the kitchen. A side-return extension, a loft conversion. They pulled back the carpets to reveal the original wood floors. The garden was landscaped by a neighbour who was doing a degree in horticulture. I remember her bright-faced enthusiasm, the plans with jazzy-coloured circles. It feels important to remember my parents' legacy. It was a building, an area of land, a set of choices, an expression of taste. A moment in time.

The rooms are mostly empty now, apart from the playroom. I shut the door on it, the sour smell of wetted-and-dried cardboard is too much. My phone rings. Max again. My phone feels sour too. It's too hot—repellent—I drop it on the floor; it thuds but doesn't break. I kick it through the bathroom door, turn on the taps.

After the last one, the process is complete. Then it can take anything from six hours to forty-eight hours to fully take hold. Be sure to be near a water source.

The bath brims over, drenching my phone. Max has called so many times that the phone is glowing, red-hot. I hear Anaïs's car pull up outside. She'll be coming in to clean any minute now. The mirror is water damaged and cloudy. My old legs have withered to almost nothing, but my new legs are strong. My neck is much longer, streamers of frills like musical notes shimmer away from my jawline. I can see everything; I can feel everything. The air, the cycle of cool and warm, the damp and dry, the singing in the reeds, the ache of the moon. I hope Anaïs isn't too upset. I like her. I've always liked her. When mum and dad were really in the thick of it (and they were really in very, very deep, really up to their eyeballs, you know?) she would come every day and check on them. Max didn't. I didn't. I feel bad about what Anaïs had to do for them, in the end. I hope she sees the note pinned to the front door. I hope she knows I appreciate her. I climb the stairs; it's hard. My hand traces the curve of the banister as it has a hundred million times. This will rot away too. The roof has holes in it that widen in every storm like screaming mouths. The holes will let in water, and the wood will swell, and the timbers and joists will eventually buckle and fall inwards. Nothing is permanent. Everyone knows that. I lower myself into the bath. The pores on my face are huge—sinkholes— reflected in the curve of the taps. The biggest pore, on the tip of my nose, becomes the pool that contains my parents. They are there, right there at the bottom, waving to me. It's a well, a deep well, I see that now. A thousand miles deep. My parents are laughing, but not kindly. I take the last tablet. Max is calling. There's a knocking at the front door, a rising crescendo.

My Two Sons

The house is too hot, so we decide to go out and walk along the cliff path; my two sons and I. They walk in front, the taller one ahead of the shorter one, both scuffing the dust from the ground in little clouds that puff into the air around their shoes. I look at their backs and wonder, again, about which son I prefer. The taller one is skinny, with lank and pale hair that grows too long. It brushes at the collar of his t-shirt. He is younger than his brother, who is stocky and serious. I have to explain this to people all of the time; it's very tiresome. People's questions are very tiresome.

Is the older son jealous of the younger one for being taller?

Is the younger son self-conscious about his height?

How do you cope with these two sons?

The shrubs on either side of the path are scorched and dry. My younger son has found a stick in the hedgerow. He swings it over the pale grasses that grow along the path. His brother wants a stick too, but he can't find one. My older son has dark eyes; he is cautious and thoughtful. I look out

164

across the bay; a dense haze hangs over the water. There are already people on the beach. I can see their skin glistening as they set out their blankets for the day. I don't know how anyone can bring themselves to do that, to still do that. There are protective measures you can take, I suppose, if you have enough money. The ships are still there. There are nine now, that's two more since last week. They remain very still; huge and dark and quiet, like dead whales.

There are nine ships now, I say to my sons.

Nine is quite a lot, says my older son.

It's not too bad, I say.

We walk this way often. If we go early in the morning, then my sons don't get too hot. We could go to the woods, I suppose, and walk in the cool shade afforded by the trees, but it's busy at this time of year. Everyone crowds along the paths, enjoying the scent of the pine and the whispering leaves. They stare at the three of us all together, so I have to hurry my sons along. We prefer places that are quieter, where we can walk at our own pace.

My older son is cautious. He stays away from the cliff-edge. I don't have to remind him of danger. My younger son is more erratic, skipping and dancing, swooshing his stick to sever the tops of the dry plants. His brother takes hold of his arm, gently, to steady him. They don't talk much to one another, but my sons have a special bond. There's a closeness between them.

It must be nice that they are so compatible, people say. *I would love to have two sons that are as compatible as yours.*

At first, I liked how envious people were. I liked that they coveted my sons. But after a while their comments and sidelong glances began to make me feel self-conscious. I wondered if this self-consciousness would seep into my two sons and damage them. That's why we came to live out here, where there are fewer people, where we can take walks in the early morning and hope not to see anyone.

My taller, younger son is up ahead at a fork in the path. He wants us to go down to the beach. I check the time. There won't be many people down there at this time, so I agree to his request. The older son nods in approval and takes the lead, making sure that he and his brother pick their way carefully down to the shingle. This beach is secluded; if you don't have a boat, or know about this path, you can only get to it at low tide. People don't tend to come here as the sand is covered in a layer of shingle and a mess of shells. People prefer sand; they like it when the stones and shells are finely ground.

My two sons clatter onto the shore. The sea washes in a hush—back and forth—over the stones.

Don't you worry about them going near the water?

Don't you worry about how the moisture in the air will affect them out there?

Don't you worry about what you would do, out there, if something went wrong?

My two sons are robust though; I don't need to worry. All of their lives I have wondered if I should worry, but you can't help your feelings, can you? Is worry a feeling? Perhaps it is something more than that.

I wanted these two sons more than anything I've ever wanted. I worked hard for them. I gave up so much; almost everything. I can't pretend things are easy, but I must help my sons take their place in the world.

The older son walks with purpose, following the meandering tide mark. The younger one is further ahead. He's crouching down, examining something on the shingle, face too close to the stones. I watch as the older one joins him. They squat on their haunches together, side by side, and the younger one pokes at the thing on the ground with his stick. The sea washes in a hush—back and forth—over the stones.

The fog of the morning has all but burned away. The water dances with grey and blue. There are kayaks weaving in between the ships. I walk over to my sons.

The younger one moves aside so that I can see what they are looking at. Something shimmers on the stones. It's about the size of a hubcap, translucent and gelatinous. Hardly there at all. My older son looks tired, like he's low on energy. I calculate how long it will take us to get back.

We have to leave soon, I tell them.

What is it? asks my older son. His brow furrows. He can't seem to look away.

It's just an animal from the sea, I say. *Nothing for us to worry about.*

Is it dying?

No. No, these things are really tough.

I don't want it to die.

168

It'll be fine, I promise. The tide will take it out again soon.

A kayak appears, in from the bay. Two men jump out and into the shallows. They're dressed in wetsuits with silver stripes on the arms. Both wear expressions of concern as they drag their boat out of the water. I know how to speak to the authorities; I've done it before. My sons have seen me do it.

The men watch us but keep their distance.

Everything OK over there? one of the men half-shouts.

Fine, I reply. *Thank you.* My sons stand up.

It's not really safe down here, the other man says. *For you—for your—*

He stops. Then starts again: *the water isn't safe*.

We're fine, I repeat. *Thank you.*

The man is walking over. My sons watch him, and then they move—quickly—so that they are standing very close to me. My older son's hands ball up into fists at his sides.

The man stops, holds open his palms to show that they are empty. My sons stand very still, watching. The man swallows, I see his Adam's apple bob in his throat.

Are they both yours? he asks. His voice is lower now that he's closer to us.

Yes, I say. I can hear the sea breaking on the shingle.

You're very lucky.

Yes, I know.

We—my wife and I—we would love to have sons like that—like yours.

A lot of people tell me the same thing.

The two officers from the kayak stare at my sons. My sons stare back. The sea animal glistens in the sunlight. I realise that the tide is going out; the creature will dry out soon unless someone scoops it up and helps it back into the water. Even then it might be too late. It might already be too late. I hate lying to my sons.

The men shift awkwardly in their wetsuits. They are both tall, like my younger son, and they are both broad-shouldered like my older son. There are decisions in life that we must all make. I know this.

We'd better be going, says one of the men. *You need to be careful down here. Those boys—your sons—they shouldn't be that close to the water.*

Thank you, officer, I say.

They pick up their kayak and head towards the cliff path, carrying it on their shoulders like pallbearers. We watch them go, my two sons and I.

When the men are out of sight, my older son takes my hand. My younger son springs away from us and returns to the sea animal. He pokes at it with his stick, gently. He is a sweet boy; I do know that.

Look! he shouts to his brother. *It's soft. Just like Ma.*

His brother doesn't reply but holds tight to my hand.

It'll die, won't it? says my older son. He turns his face up to look at me, eyes wide open to the sun which is now vast and searing above us. I can't stand it when he does that, but I let it go. I remind myself that no harm will come to him or his brother if they do that. There are all sorts of things that my sons can do that I never could, or ever will.

Yes, I say. *It will die.*

I thought so, he says. *Come on, time to go.*

The sea washes in a hush—back and forth, back and forth—over the stones. Closer now, much closer.

We head back towards the path, leaving the sea animal where we found it. As we start our ascent, I turn back to look at it again. It gleams on the foreshore like a disc of bright mirror, like a glass eye.

The Unreliable Nature Writer Stands Outside To Smoke A Cigarette, While Everyone Else Is Inside Dancing

– Ah there you are. Look, I'm sorry about earlier. I feel like I said something weird—

Oh—did you? In what way?

– OK, maybe *you* said something weird then. I feel like something weird happened.

We were just talking about your job. That's all. And then you were very excited about the drinks. You knocked over quite a lot of glassware at one point, too, but I don't think anyone noticed.

– Oh yeah, yeah sorry. It's just the booze. Or the occasion. I don't have the stamina for this sort of thing anymore.

Would you like a cigarette?

– Oh god no. Oh, well, maybe? Actually, no. No thanks. No. I won't.

It might help you relax?

– Maybe. I worry about where it will lead though.

What do you mean?

– Sometimes I think that we don't have free will at all. Sometimes I feel like I'm just going through the motions—

Maybe that's because you are—

—What? Oh, well yes. I probably am. Like, society puts us on these tramlines and we're told we can get off at any time, but we can't, not really. Not once the tram is really going, hurtling along, gathering speed with us all trapped inside. Yeah, fuck it, I will have one.

Everyone feels trapped. I feel like I'm in a sort of frozen state from time to time.

– Frozen state, yes! I feel like I'm in a cage. Maybe you'll tell me that everyone feels like that too.

I don't know. I don't know everyone.

– Fair enough. What's your cage like then? What's the Unreliable Nature Writer's cage like? You seem pretty carefree to me.

174

Oh, I care about lots of things. You do too, surely?

– Like what?

I don't know, your wife, your kids, your house, your equity, your health. Those are all things to care about, I guess.

– Yes I suppose that's all true, maybe I shouldn't be so—

And yet.

– And yet.

Why do you think you're so unhappy?

– Who said I was unhappy? How can you possibly tell how happy I am?

Sorry.

– It's been a long day.

Anyway, that's not your fault if you're unhappy.

– I'm fine, actually. Or maybe not. I don't know.

OK.

– Say I *was* unhappy. What's the solution then?

You could leave.

– What?

You could leave. Right now.

– No I couldn't! That's absurd.

You could. You could go down these steps here, through that patio and the ornamental rose garden. You could leave your suit jacket inside, with your phone in the pocket, and just slip away into the night. You could get on a train somewhere. How much money is in your bank account? A fair bit I reckon.

– More than ten thousand if I were to hazard a guess. Something like that, quite a lot more, to be honest, but it's all tied up in bonds and share dividends, and—

There you go. You could start again on that kind of money.

– Yes. Yes I suppose I could, but what would I do?

You could go somewhere with poor phone reception. Somewhere by the sea.

– Oh wow, yes! I could go to the middle of nowhere, couldn't I? Like...like...the north of Scotland. I could work the land, just me and my hands and my tools.

Tools?

– Yes, I'd get some.

And is that really the middle of nowhere?

– Oh yes, hardly anyone lives up there. It'd be brilliant, imagine acres and acres of land overlooking the sea, waking up every morning and walking the land, tending to the sheep that graze there, coming back to the house each evening to make a fire. That does sound idyllic. A simpler way of living. I can't say I'm not tempted. I wonder if I'd get bored there, by myself—

There would be other people there though, you know.

– Oh, really?

Well, yeah. It's a place where people actually live.

– Right, yes, hardly anyone though. But I suppose you're right. Still, I'd keep myself to myself, wouldn't I? And the locals would accept me, in time, I'm sure.

Oh, yeah. Sure.

– I do worry that I might get bored though.

Yes.

– And lonely.

Yes.

– And regretful.

Yes. And perhaps a deep disappointment that the fantasy hasn't matched up to the reality.

– I feel that way now, though, a lot of the time.

Well, all you have to do is go down those steps, head for the exit. Oh—are you OK?

– Yes. Sorry. Yes, I'm fine.

It just looks like you're—

– What? No, I mean—I think it's just a long time since I smoked.

And there's quite a lot of blood on your shirt. There, see?

– Oh, that's just from the broken glass—cut my hand! —I tried to help them, but they weren't very happy with me.

It's OK if you want to cry.

– I know, I know.

It's a wedding. They bring out the worst in us. Like Christmas.

– I know. I'm sorry. I'm fine, really. So many stars out here in the countryside. Isn't it lovely to look up and feel so small?

I hate it.

– What? How can you say that?

I get vertigo when I think about the solar system.

– Right, sure. Of course.

The weight of all those stars, just hanging there above us. Gives me the creeps.

– I can't, you know. I can't go.

I know.

Cephalopod

You have to braise it until it's tender. It's not supposed to be flash fried in the same way as you would a squid. That's a mistake people make. You could deep fry it in tempura batter I suppose; that'd be quite nice. But it has to be treated differently to a squid. Totally different cellular structure. Totally different animal.

She picks up a coil of purple meat. There are suckers on it. It curls away from her fork — tapering elegantly — in a frozen gesture. The glossy sauce drips from her fork, the droplets land on the white tablecloth, bleeding darkly. She eats it in one go.

Oh yes. Very tender. I catch glimpses of dark flesh churning inside her mouth as she speaks.

What's yours like? she says, jabbing her knife in the air near my plate. *Some bottom-feeder probably. Some shit-eater.* She laughs; swallows. *The food here has been extolled for centuries but it's all just citrus and fat and salt. No special wizardry.*

I know better than to contradict her. The other diners, bathed in the light from the glittering sea, are casting sidelong glances at this tiny, frail woman as she chomps and laughs her way through her meal.

Her body has shrunk over the years. Caved in on itself. Her brain too, making her crotchety; cantankerous. She asks questions and then gets bored halfway through the answer, asking another one and then another and another, until they stack up unevenly and she can't remember where we started. I visit less and less.

I'm so bored of it all, she says. *I want a Chinese takeaway! I want ham, egg and chips! I want a digestive biscuit, for fuck's sake!*

I remind myself that she's nearly dead. Fading away, they said. She doesn't look it though. Right now, she looks vital. There's a glow in her papery skin. Her movements are easy. Maybe it's the evening light playing tricks. The sun hovers—bored and bloated from the day—ready to drop into the sea.

The sea is boiling hot, nowadays.

She looks past me—beyond the other tables just like ours, covered with paper tablecloths that flap occasionally in the sea breeze—towards the water. She's been talking about the rising sea temperatures a lot during this stay. She likes to mention it a little too loudly when out in public, so that heads turn. I ask—quietly—that she lay off the hyperbole, but she waves away my protest with a forkful of meat.

You're in denial, aren't you? she says, almost gleefully. *You'd really rather not know about this stuff.*

She wants to talk with her mouth full. She wants to argue about how much hotter the sea is going to get. She wants me to listen to how this affects her, how this will affect her work. She talks like she'll be around to see it; all of that life cooking in the sea, floating—distended, tepid—to the surface to bleach in the sun. The fishermen coming back empty-handed, people starving in the ports; the collapse of it all. She still works, in emeritus, although she's long retired. She accepts that much, at least. She's got more than enough money to last her until the end; money that she wields at me once or twice a year by booking these trips. To get here I took the train and the ferry. She didn't want me to fly.

Flying is the one thing we can all do without, she said. *There's no need for it. No one needs to get anywhere quickly anymore. Speed is a poison. Urgency is a poison.*

*

They have strong, beak-like jaws but the rest of their bodies are soft. They have three hearts: one to pump blood to the head and two smaller ones to pump blood to the gills. They have a brain, but a large number of their neurons are distributed throughout their arms.

How could any animal do all of that with their legs? she would shout at me if she was in the wrong mood. *It's arms. Arms!*

I learned how to reach high up for the littlest saucepan; how to boil an egg for her breakfast; tuck myself in at night. I learned that I had to bring her two tablets to her in bed at noon.

She would say, *it's my work: my baby*. It was more than that. Her work was part of her; woven through her nervous system. The week after I left home, she did too, packing up her biggest suitcase, hauling it into a taxi with her lean arms. She was offered teaching and research posts in coastal regions across the world. It was an exciting time for her, and she was still young, as she kept reminding me. She would call me if she moved house, rarely in between.

The large number of neurons in their arms means that they can exert very precise control over their limbs. Their skin is covered with chromatophores; cells that can change colour and reflect the light. They use camouflage better than any other animal. They have great dexterity and sensitivity; they can reach into tiny crevices, feeling about in the gloom for prey. Their arms have sensation for hours after they have been severed from the body.

She collected bright minds, had friends over most nights. Working groups that become parties that would go on into the small hours. I was to stay away when she was working. She couldn't be two things at once, she said. But I learned how to creep into stairwells and hallways, feeling my way in the dark. I learned how to silence my breathing so that I could listen. I would stay in the dark shadows of doorways so long that I forgot who I was. One night, I slithered past the living room door and out into the cool of the garden, laughter and music boiling inside the house. I let my feet brush through the wet, blackened grass, right to the end of the garden. I leaned over the barbed wire fence, snagging the cotton of my nightdress, the points of rusted metal digging into my stomach as I peered out across the lane. The main road shone like a river in the moonlight. She never noticed that I was gone.

The lifestyle suited her. The research laboratories and lecture theatres were always air-conditioned, and she liked to go out in the evenings, to laugh and smoke with whomever was around. She was lauded everywhere she went. Students, colleagues, lovers. If they left her, she would just replace them, grow them back.

A therapist once said, *do you feel as though you give her a hard time?* And I got up and left the consultation room, slamming the door on my way out. But now, whatever pain was there has ebbed away now. Time rolls in and out like the tide and washes everything clean. Memories float high above me now.

*

This morning I woke up just after five, I got up and crept out of her apartment, tiptoeing past the door to her room where she lay on her back with her arms by her sides. The machines clicked and exhaled with her. I watch the thin cage of her chest rising and falling. Her mouth open, her hair spread out across the pillow like seaweed. I know that I'll be sad when she's gone. I let the door clang shut and went down the communal stairs. Outside the air was dark blue and tender. The first fronds of sunlight pushing their way around street corners. I found myself walking towards the harbour.

At that hour, the only people on the streets were the men and boys on the boats. The guttural chatter, the fizz of the radio, the smell of the engine oil. It had been a while since I'd been close to a man. I wondered if it had been longer for me than for her. My back to a wall, I watched their smooth arms hauling nets, gutting fish, opening and filling polystyrene containers, scooping ice, closing, resealing and lifting. Repeating again and again; stacking and lifting and slicing and shucking. An elliptical cycle; enacting generations of muscle memory. Old men in cut-off jeans, young men with slick haircuts, some thin, some strapping, some fat and wheezing, some smoking, some shouting, some with grief-burdened shoulders, some springing from deck to harbour wall—nimbly—like they might evaporate in the rising heat of the morning. Everything full of grace; everything fluid.

Their intelligence is in their nervous system, she would always say. *You can't compare their intelligence to ours. Their intelligence is like several of us, all working together, intuitively.*

The catch glistened in the boxes. Smooth flat ovals; eyes still glossy and bright; mottled torpedoes; ghostly fins. Tentacles moved and shuddered, cascading and careening over each other as they were sealed into boxes. The sun inflated, dancing in the water, reflecting the hulls of the fishing boats and the metal of the men's tools. I left, hungry and sick all at once.

She was awake when I returned, bustling about the apartment, the breathing machines all tucked away. She had made coffee and stood on the balcony with her back to me, illuminated by the high sun. I could see through her dressing gown; through her gauzy skin and straight through to her bones. A jolt of a memory: walking along a cold beach with her, my tiny hand wrapped with hers, picking up dogfish egg cases—mermaid's purses—and holding them up to the light. They were dry and brittle.

It's our last day, she said, without turning around. *We'll eat something delicious.*

Much later, we walked back down to the harbour. The men on the boats were still there but the activity was different, slower. Some older men sat at a metal table in front of bowls piled with empty shells. One of the younger ones sang along to the radio. Gulls flopped on and off the harbour wall.

Too early for supper. Let's walk along the beach.

We found the slipway and made our way through the last of the day trippers, and the locals sunning themselves after work. It's safe to do that now, if you take the right tablets; if you accept that you'll die faster. Along with tobacco smoking, it feels like no one minds dying very much anymore.

We walked out along the headland, where the ocean scurried up the foreshore, dragging sand and seaweed and hapless fragments of crab shell back with it—repeating and repeating—making gentle progress inland each time.

She tucked her arm into mine. It felt brittle.

Have I ever told you about what they do with their young?

No.

The mother goes into this sort of fugue state while she incubates the eggs. Nestles down around them. It takes everything she has to nurture them during the gestation period, to the point where it causes her cells to break down.

What happens after that? To the mother, I mean.

Well, she effectively self-destructs. In order to give life to the eggs.

Oh. Wow.

Yes. 'Wow', indeed. Some people refer to it as a sort of 'cellular suicide' but I think that's rather overly dramatic, don't you?

I suppose so, yes, I said. *Suicide is something melancholic. Do animals feel melancholy?*

Suicide is born from futility, not necessity. I think the mother accepts her fate and just gets on with it. Something innate and within her commands that her cells break down, and that's it: no looking back.

Is acceptance something they are capable of? I said, feeling my chest tighten, *is fate something they know, something they can comprehend?* I don't know why I kept asking questions. I don't know what I was trying to get her to say.

We don't know. But one of my theories is that motherhood— for many species—is a process of continual acceptance of one's fate. An act of attempting to delay death and then realising it's impossible.

I turned to look at her, with her hollow face beneath its huge sunglasses, her bobbed halo of hair ablaze in the late afternoon sun. She stared straight ahead. Her legs are mapped with veins, there's no muscle there anymore. I marvelled at how she could continue to walk with such purpose.

Afterwards we made our way back up to the harbour and found this place. I ordered something that translated roughly as 'white fish and sauce'. I knew, before she did, what she was going to order.

*

The sun slinks off. She's eaten everything. I've hardly touched mine. I can't stop thinking about that mother, hunkering down around her eggs. Why would anyone choose that? The waiter comes and clears our plates, and she strikes up a conversation with him. She speaks his language rapidly and with absolute accuracy. She makes no attempt at an accent, but then she never has. He asks her if she has enjoyed her meal. I can't quite keep up, but I think she's telling him that it was the most delicious meal she's ever eaten; that it was a *most superior creature*. She gestures with grandiosity, looping her slender arm in the air as she reaches into her bag for her cigarettes. The waiter's eyes dart between mine and his colleague's. Her voice grows louder and louder. She says that it was like eating a divine being; that this was a godlike creature from another world that no one will ever fully understand. Some of the other diners look over, she is saying that now she is godlike because this animal—this marvel of evolution, this divine creature—is inside her. She's addressing the whole patio now, has turned her chair to the tables next to ours. I excuse myself, making my way towards the bathroom, her voice still clear and sharp behind me. I slide between the tables and out across the boulevard, making my way down the slipway and onto the beach. The sand is cool. The ocean is cooler still and viscous—bluish-black—as though brimming with ink.

Paddling Pool

It's not unethical to buy one, despite what some people say. Sure, there's too much plastic in the world, too much material, too many petrochemicals, but no one has told us definitively that it's not OK. They would have banned them, anyway.

It's completely fine if you want to walk to the hypermarket to buy one, making your way along the grass verge of the main road, cars skimming past your waist. On the box there is a picture of the inflated pool, filled to the top. Happy children, sitting in the water, splashing around. You can ignore that if you want. The children's teeth are far too white anyway. The sides of the pool are kind of sexy when they're inflated, but you might not be able to work out why. Best not to think too much about that.

It's a long walk to the hypermarket. You could walk through fields and behind railway lines, balancing along the side of the road that leads you into acres of car park that shimmers in the heat. When you get inside, the air is cool and feels soft on your skin. You might want to have a browse around the dazzling aisles, seeing as how you're there now,

the thing in its box wedged under your arm. You might want
to slide out a baguette from the bakery section, allow its thin
plastic cover to slip off. You might gnaw on this as you make
your way through the hypermarket. The bread will be crusty
on the outside and will cut little abrasions into the corners of
your mouth. The inside is fluffy and soft. You imagine lying
down on a white bed.

You might find yourself in the drinks aisle, picking up a
bottle of gin. You might put it back, then pick it up again.
Making your way home, it's OK if you want to swig from the
bottle as you go, the drivers in their silent cars ignoring you as
you walk along the verge, where walking isn't really allowed.

When you get home, the gin might be half-finished, and
the pool will need inflating. But you'll take a minute to think
about what you've done, what you are about to do. You might
reason with yourself. It's hot. It's extremely hot and you
need to cool down. Things have been stressful recently. You
need to take some time. It really is very hot. Did you really
need to buy the pool? You're a grown woman for god's sake.
There's no one else here. It's just you. What are you going to
do with it afterwards? What's your long-term plan here? It's
probably OK. It's probably fine. The pool exists and existed
before you owned it. You may as well own it, someone's
got to. The petrochemicals are in the world already. And it's
here, flat and expectant, unfurled across your patio.

There's a pump somewhere, takes ages to find it, doesn't work that well. You could actually use your mouth for a bit, and you do and that summertime plastic smell floods into everything, along with the blue and the warmth and for a while this breathing in and out with your eyes closed is actually all you might need. But then your mouth gets dry and the garden starts to spin and maybe all this gin in this heat was inadvisable but what else were you supposed to do? Really, what can any of us ever really do?

When it's ready you get the hose and fill it up. It really is as simple as that. You can get in and the water will cool you. You can stretch your arms along the sides and rest your cheek there too. Stroke the side of it with your fingertips. Your skin, in the water, is paler somehow; translucent. You could think about jellyfish in the Mediterranean, soft and elegant, moving through the aquamarine with no effort at all. Your legs are weightless, just like that jellyfish. Put on your sunglasses and turn your face up towards the sun. You can get your gin and put ice cubes in it. It will be soothing. You can stay there all afternoon if you like. No one will mind. No one's here and that's how you wanted it. No one's here to tell you they need you, or to tell you to pick up your stuff from the floor, or to ask you to make them a drink, or to take your hand in theirs. You made these choices, which were—absolutely—the correct ones. You might go inside, your legs dripping onto the kitchen floor, get the (nearly empty—really?) bottle of gin, and pour it all out into your glass. Doesn't matter. Everything's OK.

Of course, after a while the sun will move across the sky and the patio will be eaten by shade, and your neighbours will come outside into their garden with their yappy dog and their gritted-teeth argument, and someone somewhere will be practising the violin with their windows open and the scales will claw their way up your spine and into your brain. And then the next day it will rain, and the pool will crumple and sigh as the air inside cools and decompresses. It will sag. The smooth walls will wrinkle quietly, leaning in toward each other. Insects will crash into it and drown. The bees will be baffled by the dancing light that strobes across the patio. They will fall into the blue; choking and wriggling before looping slowly, around and around. It will live in the garage after that, with spiders laying eggs in its dark folds. The plastic will take thousands of years to decompose, and before that scraps of it will wash through the soil, mixing with the grains of dirt and sand, until they find their way out to sea. You might, years later, starving, dragging yourself along the beach in the unbearable heat, you might discover a fish, partially dried out on the orange sand. Peeling away at its skin, you might find microscopic parts of your paddling pool inside. But there's no way you'll ever be able to tell if it's the same one, so don't worry about that now.

As Far North as it Goes

1. A series of islands in the North Sea gets in touch

We've never met, but I know all about you. I know things have been difficult recently; impossible, even. I think you need some time, some distance.

If you want, you could take that device in your hand and switch it off. That's right. Power off. Now, put it somewhere. A drawer maybe. Or on top of the fridge. There now. That was easy wasn't it?

Have you got sensible shoes, something you can walk in? Good. Get those ready. Find socks that cushion your feet properly, not those thin ones you wear for work. Dig around for some that are thicker. Put them on. You've got your raincoat, haven't you? And you've packed your bag. You don't need much. A few changes of clothes; a toothbrush and toothpaste; your glasses.

Take out all of the cash you have in your account. I'll wait here, don't worry. Snap the card in half. Put the two halves in your pocket.

Leave as early as you can, pull the door shut very carefully behind you. No one will hear it. If they do, they'll just roll over and go back to sleep. Leave your keys.

It'll be cold, probably raining. That's why you'll need your raincoat. Use the cash you took out earlier to buy a train ticket to Bristol. I know, it's not that far, but when you're there you can change trains and go to Edinburgh. From there, go to Inverness and then to Thurso. Why do you need to go to Thurso? Well, it's just a thought. You hate flying, remember. This is going to take a long time.

Twenty-seven hours it'll take. But think about all those trains. Think about all that land you'll cross. All that time to look out of the window as everything rushes past. Think about the silence inside your head.

But I'm getting ahead of myself.

Right, where were we? You've left the house. Good. The front door closed behind you. Don't think about the key. There's a bit of a walk to the station, but you can take the path along by the river. At dawn it's quite nice. Have a look, see if you can spot a water vole. They're quite common along here. Yes, look; there's one. All you needed to do was look. Pick your way through that little bit of woodland that runs along near the railway line. No one will see you. There are

196

birds nesting in there. I can't see them; I don't know what type of bird they are. You could find out if you went to the library, but you'll probably forget. It's quite liberating not having your phone, isn't it? Not having to look things up every five minutes. See how much calmer you feel now. Breathe in slowly. Breathe out slowly too. There now.

No headphones. No device. Cash, no cards. That reminds me, take the two halves of your card out of your pocket and go a little way into the woodland, just into the tree line, that's it. Now take one of the cards and stuff it into the earth, bury it in there. That's it. Then take the other half and head back down to the path, where you can skim it into the river. See the way it flashes red and then swoops into the water? You're not getting that back.

Do you think it's strange that I would ask you to do this? Plastic takes hundreds of years to break down in the soil, I know. There are particles in the sand; fragments of rock and bone and shell and house bricks and smooth glass and tiny jewels of plastic, all mixed up together. But I don't want you to worry about that now.

The train will be there at 6:05. You're early enough for the commuters not to be a problem. Some of them are there, men in suits with tired baggy eyes. Beige dry pastries in front of them; watery coffee in metal mugs to keep it hot. These things all come from the earth. There are base elements for everything.

Remember 'Animal, Vegetable, Mineral' from when you were a child? You used to try and find obscure objects or abstract ideas that the others had to guess. Fog, for example.

It's a mineral, your father would say. And you would ask why.

And he would say: Well, it's not an animal or a vegetable, is it?

What about an oyster? you would say.

An oyster is an animal, but only just. Some people don't believe they are sentient.

Surely something is sentient or not, you would think to yourself. It can't be a matter of opinion.

Don't be alarmed. Don't ask me how I know all this. It feels like we are supposed to be together, doesn't it? It feels like we have always known each other.

Look out of the window: the sun is trying to come up. There are rabbits in the hedgerows by the railway lines. Too close to the train; unafraid. There are deer in the middle of this field. There, see? A doe and a fawn. They're gone now. They disappear. It's so easy for them to do that.

The sun will be high by the time you change trains. It will be the middle of the morning, and you'll have a long way to go. There's a newspaper that someone left behind, You won't need to read it. The news no longer applies to you. Look out of the window as the city skids away. Think about those deer that you saw. You lean your head against the window, shut your eyes, let the light pass over them. Red, black, red, black.

The north feels different to the south, doesn't it? Not just because it's unfamiliar. The land changes too, the geology, the wildlife. Keep going. You've got money in your pocket. That's all you need. No one knows where you are.

You might be wondering why I'm so focused on cash. You wouldn't get very far without it. You need cash because your card transactions can be traced. We'll be living in a cashless society soon and everything will be traceable, everything recorded. Some people, that man over there in his pinstripe suit thinks that this is a good thing, that we should all have our financial activity monitored and recorded. But I am unsure about cash. The physical is often more powerful than the conceptual.

You'll arrive in Edinburgh around 6pm, twelve hours after you've started.

You don't like Edinburgh. You travelled up there when you were eighteen for an interview at the art school, hauling your portfolio on the train, sweating, checking your eyeliner compulsively to see if it had smudged. You waited in a high-ceilinged vestibule, trying to control your heart rate. The interviewers were austere and bored. Your interview had been the last of the day. Before you got the train home you bought four cans of cider and drank them before falling asleep sitting up. You arrived back down south, stiff and tired. An elderly man stared at you from the opposite seat, his fingers nicotine-yellow on the inside, his neck sad and drooping softly downwards. I'm sorry that didn't work out. You think about that a lot, don't you. About how things would have been different if that had worked out.

But that's all in the past now. You don't even have time to leave the station in Edinburgh, so if you like, you can pretend it's not there. That this is some other city. Rotterdam for example, or Paris. Remember Paris? Remember how you hate Paris so much more than Edinburgh? See, things aren't so bad now are they? You're just tired, I know. It's alright.

The next train goes from Edinburgh to Inverness. It takes around four hours. See how quickly the fields give way to forests. The sky is bigger up here, the air is cleaner, can you feel it? There it goes, rolling on forever. The sun is setting and it's beautiful. It feels very remote doesn't it? It'll be dark by the time you arrive in Inverness. The train to Thurso isn't until the morning.

Don't worry, we can leave it there for today. You go into the town and find a place to stay.

2. I spend the night in Inverness

It turns out it's quite hard to book a hotel without a credit or debit card. At the Mercure Hotel they shake their heads, their arms stiffly by their sides. That's OK, I reason, it's too much money anyway. I go into the Premier Inn. The man on the reception desk has perfectly groomed eyebrows. An angelic sheen of highlighter skims across his cheekbones; the delicate fade of his haircut shimmers in the fluorescent light. He looks at me askance when I say I only have cash. I don't want to make him feel uncomfortable. If he's uncomfortable then he might sweat, and if he sweats, his makeup will run, and I couldn't bear to do that to him. So, I ask if he thinks anywhere might let me stay if I only have cash. He looks online. There's a guest house, he says, called the River View Hotel. I smile and he smiles back. His teeth are slightly crooked and very white.

The River View Hotel isn't next to the river. It's in a side street of terraced houses. It has a bay window, a canvas awning and a swinging sign at the front.

Yes, I'm on holiday, yeah just one night. Getting a train to Thurso in the morning.

The guesthouse manager is called Linda—she sits at a desk just inside the front door. Her manicured nails click-clack on the laptop as she books me in. She tells me that the coach to Thurso is faster than the train and follows an A-road that runs along the coast.

You can see the North Sea from the coach, Linda says.

I want to see the North Sea. That's one of the things I'm here for, to look at the North Sea. I didn't realise it before but that's all I want to do. I want to look at the North Sea on my own. I want to look at the expanse of it. I'll look at the North Sea as I go on the coach to Thurso and when I get to Thurso I'll decide what to do next. I have time.

I've booked the cheapest, smallest room in the River View Hotel. It's a single room with yellowish-magnolia walls. The bedding on the single bed is crisp and ironed, white with a bright red-and-blue flower print. The print is too big for the room. There's a dark veneered wardrobe and set of shelves with a TV perched on the top, a fire door, a tiny en-suite; all of it immaculately clean. It's cold outside and the heating is up very high. I go over to the window, and realise that yes, there is a view of the river from here. It trails its way along the side of the road, wide grey water and wide grey pavement, the sky above it darkening to a blue-black. I open the window and breathe in the outside air. It's metallic and alive.

It's still early and I'm hungry, so I leave the River View Hotel and go out into the night. I walk along the side of the river, which is far too wide. It feels like there should be more city. Maybe there was more at one time; maybe the river encroaches on it every year, but so very slowly that the inhabitants don't notice. The mountains sit, flat and too big, against the darkening sky. I have a map of the town centre from the River View Hotel in my hand, it's hard to read in the glow from the streetlights.

An off-licence, brimming with acidic light. I go in and buy four cans of cider and a sandwich. The white triangles of bread look like dentist's putty. Inside is something yellow. It all goes into a blue carrier bag that frets in the breeze when I leave the shop.

My map tells me that Inverness means 'mouth of the Ness'. It tells me that there are some islands upstream of the city centre. I open one of the cans of cider and get my bearings.

There's a narrow footbridge, ornate wrought iron and painted in peeling white that glows in the light cast by the orange street lamps. Underneath, the river churns forward. I remember reading somewhere that the Scottish lochs are the murkiest bodies of water in the British Isles due to their high peat content. That's why the Loch Ness monster legend continues to survive; no one will ever be able to see into the water long enough to know for sure. I leave the footbridge and walk into the dark woodland.

A fallen tree trunk has been carved into the shape of a snake. Its surface has been worn smooth. My map tells me that children come here to climb on it during the daytime. It's dark now, but there are lights twinkling between the trees. The city is still there, bright against the landscape. I sit on the tree trunk. I drink another two cans of cider and eat one of the triangles.

It's harder to find my way in the dark after the cider. I don't know what the time is. I follow the lights. They are like hard jewels. My eyes water in the wind. It's always cold in Scotland. October is my favourite month. I wonder if this is because of what October is like here. If I had grown up on the other side of the world, maybe I wouldn't have liked October so much. October is a construct though—just something monks decided on—so maybe it isn't October that I like at all, maybe it's something more fleeting than that. I find the bridge and open the last can of cider. I take the second white triangle from the packaging and hurl it into the water.

*

I forget to draw the curtains in my room, so I wake up to the grey and the sounds of traffic. Everywhere has a rush hour. Everywhere in the world. The paper map is scrunched next to my face. I'm still in my clothes from the night before. I take a shower in the tiny bathroom and dress and go downstairs. The breakfast is included in the price. The clock on the wall says 7:35.

A thin woman, with sleek hair, tied up so severely that it pulls her face back, clinks teacups against saucers as she sets them out. My teeth itch. There are large glass mugs of juice: orange, pink, red like blood. I sit down and the woman smiles at me, asks me if I want tea or coffee? I ask for tea. I ask for a cooked breakfast. I want to get my money's worth. I'm the only one there so it comes extremely quickly and I eat it all. In Scotland the sausages are flat and square. I wonder if they use different pigs — Scottish pigs — to make these sausages. Where am I going now?

Rush hour is over, and the wind rolls in off the river as I walk to Inverness bus station. I have eight hundred pounds in my pocket. This is only just dawning on me now. The weight of the money, the weight of everything. I keep walking.

3. The Coach to Thurso

This road feels like the only road in the world.

   Cheap cider gives you a headache the next day. I should remember that. The hills are in front, burgundy and dark green. The road is lined with gorse bushes. The yellow of the gorse flowers reminds me of the triangle-sandwich from last night and makes me feel sick. On my right side is the sea, skimming along, racing the coach.

   The hills in the Scottish Highlands look nothing like anywhere else in the world. They look like cushions. I rest my head against them through the coach window; imagine my face on the mountain-cushions. No one is sitting next to me. Most people get the train to Thurso from Inverness. Or they drive. This is good for me; I want to be on my own.

   The sun sends shards of light onto the surface of the North Sea, but the water doesn't want that. It twists and throws the light away. The sea needs the sun for the marine life to thrive. What kind of a mother would starve her own children?

   'We know more about outer space than we do about the bottom of the sea.' That can't be true. Must be a myth. We know everything about everywhere. I get vertigo when I think about the sea. I can smell chlorine from the toilet on the coach and it reminds me of going to the swimming pool on Saturday mornings. A rectangle of aquamarine. Laughter dissolving on blue and white tiles.

When I was a child, I had a recurring dream that our house had flooded and was filled from floor to ceiling with water. The house became like a fish tank. My parents, happy in their swimsuits, could breathe underwater. I remember my mother in a purple high-leg costume, rippling through the kitchen and up the stairs. There was seaweed in there too, and dolphins. The whole house smelled of chlorine.

There are dolphins in the sea off the coast of the Scottish Highlands. Pilot whales too, which are actually a type of dolphin. I don't know how I know that. My head is pounding. I wish I had bought some water before I got on the coach. I look out at the North Sea and imagine what it would be like to walk into it. To take off all my clothes and walk down to the shore and straight into the water without breaking my stride. I squint to see if I can see anyone on the beaches as we roll past, but the road veers inland and we turn our backs on the beach.

I'm two years old, I'm walking along the beach near my parents' house. I'm running as fast as I can. They are walking behind me, hand in hand.

I'm eight or nine. I swim out to a lagoon by myself and haul myself up onto the rocks. If I angle my body, the beach disappears behind the rising towers of granite and it's like no one is there.

I'm thirteen. It's too hot. I put my head between my knees and draw circles in the sand with a piece of driftwood.

I'm older; an adult. It's night-time. I follow the beach as it slopes down into the black water.

I jolt awake at a stop. People get on and off. No one wants to sit next to me. I shut my eyes again.

I would never swim in the sea if my feet couldn't touch the seabed. A whale never touches the seabed, or at least it doesn't look like it should. Do whales float or sink when they die?

There are new people on the coach now; tourists. A North American accent, two North American accents. A Scottish one now.

…Are you going for the whale watching?

Oh yes, yes.

Some lovely wildlife in this part of the world.

Absolutely, we've been planning this trip for years.

Not just whales, mind you. Seals, dolphins, all sort of birds—

We're very excited about the birdlife, it's a passion of ours.

Ah, yes, lots of people come for the birdlife.

*

I'm in a boat on the sea. It's dusk and I have to spend the night here. The anchor is down. There's a breeze, but it's not cold. I'm on my own. There's something in the water. Something huge, but it's not frightening. I feel it through my feet and the fibreglass hull.

I wake up with the sun burning my skin and I peel my face away from the coach window. We're inland again. The voices are silent now. I look behind me and see the American couple, sun-visors and beige money belts and fleeces. They stare out of the window as we curve back towards the sea. Across the aisle is a middle-aged man in a checked shirt and jeans, walking boots. He's scrolling on his phone. A hiking backpack sits next to him on the seat.

Fields now, and moorland. The land flattens out. Low dry stone walls with lemon-yellow and peach lichen line the roadside. A mist rolls in, enveloping us.

You get all four seasons in a day up here, says the Scottish man with the phone and the backpack.

Oh yes, says the American woman, *most certainly*.

We arrive at Wick. People get off, others get on. The three behind me stay put. I see the people of Wick going about their lives. I wonder what it would take for me to be one of them.

It's a lovely part of the world, Wick, says the Scottish man. I whip my head around, terrified that I've been talking aloud. He makes eye contact with me briefly, and I realise he's talking to the American couple again.

Yes, it seems like it would be a great place to live. The woman is the only one talking to him now. Her husband turns his head and looks out of the window.

Fields and sheep scud past as we leave Wick. I'm starving. We're away from the ocean again, I try and remember the map and the coach route that I saw at the bus station at Inverness. We move across the land and a pine forest appears, neat and orderly, shielding the sea from me. There are squat farm buildings, bracing against the wind and rain, hunched and secretive. The land and sea work in conspiracy here.

4. Thurso to Scrabster

Excuse me, hi. This is quite a weird question perhaps, but I'm just wondering if you can tell me what comes next?

What do you mean?

Sorry, I mean, what's next along the road, if I keep following it.

What, this road here? The A-road?

Yeah. I got a coach here from Inverness, but this is the end of the line.

Well, where d'you want to get to?

I'm just travelling around really.

From England?

Yes.

You here for the whale watching?

No, well, not especially. I didn't really know about it.

Ah, well, the whale-watching is why most tourists come up at this time of year. It used to only be in the summer, but there are more whales nowadays.

Oh right.

Yeah, they say the oceans have got warmer, so the whales are up here later in the year.

Makes sense, I guess.

But I was looking online and there's this whole conspiracy around it, saying that Northern European governments have done something to deliberately herd the whales up here, you know, to boost tourism.

That doesn't sound likely, is it even possible to herd whales?

Ah, well they can do pretty much anything with technology these days can't they. I wouldn't be surprised if they were all holograms or something, it's not like you ever see one up close.

Yeah, right.

D'you need a place to stay? There's a list of guest houses we keep behind the bar.

No, that's alright, thanks. I'm just passing through.

Suit yourself. This road leads over to the next town. Not much there. Just the ferry port and some houses.

After all those hours on the coach, walking feels like floating. Or maybe it's the sandwich I had in the pub, or the lager, or both, that buoys me. But either way I skim along the road, the road that's carried me from Inverness, the road that bears me forward like a wave beneath me. The sun is out, glittering on the tarmac. I can't see the North Sea, but I know it's there.

The village of Scrabster appears out of nowhere; the harbour, the ferry port, and the sea step around a corner all at once and take me by the hand. Beyond the ferry port the houses sit patiently by the water, snug against the cliff. I feel the weight of the cash in my pocket. I walk into the passenger terminal and buy a single ticket to Stromness in Orkney.

5. The ferry to Orkney

The seats on the ferry are upholstered with the same fabric as the seats on the coach. The fabric is more worn and gives off a smell of diesel and cigarettes and stale cooking oil. I climb the stairs to the deck outside. There is hardly anyone here. Two teenagers roll cigarettes. Bitten nails and flaking polish. There are clusters of people leaning against the railings, watching the port shrink back behind us. There's the man from the coach. Right there. The man with the red and black checked shirt and the stone-wash jeans. He must be in his late fifties, grey curly hair and beard, wide hands like he's had a life carrying heavy objects. He stares out at the water like he knows it. He's travelling light, just that one backpack. He's probably a local, probably does this journey all the time. The backpack doesn't mean anything though. My bag is smaller than his and I don't look like a local. I wouldn't know what I looked like. This man will tell me what I need to do, he'll be able to help me. I don't really want any help. I walk over and stand against the railings anyway, a metre away from him. He smiles at me, politely, like he doesn't want to talk. I picked up a paper map in the ferry terminal. I get it out and the edges flap violently in the wind like a netted seabird. I fold it back up and stuff it away in my bag.

Your first time travelling to Orkney? says the man.

Yes, I say and turn to him.

You here for the whale watching?

Yes.

He nods, smiling. He wants me to be there for the whale watching.

You know, he continues, *I was out here on this ferry crossing a few weeks back and there was a sighting.*

Someone told me earlier that there was some kind of conspiracy by northern Europe's tourist board to herd whales north.

He laughs, I can see fillings, black and gold. Treasure at the back of his mouth. *Oh, that's one I've not heard before. That's a good one.*

Are you here for the whale watching? I ask him.

No, well, not really. He turns back to look at the sea, and the white carpet of wash that streams behind the boat. *I've been visiting my daughter in Scotland.*

My stomach sinks when he says *daughter.* I don't know why. I don't know where that comes from. But now he wants to chat. He tells me he's lived in the same place for twenty years and is retired now but used to work on the ferries. He's a musician too, but his passion, his great love, is beachcombing.

I have a couple of places on the west coast that I visit regularly, like I mean, every other day or so. It's best after a big storm, there's so much to sift through.

What sort of stuff? Like driftwood?

Yes, but also animal bones—skulls of birds and seals, that sort of thing—or things that have fallen overboard from ships, nets for example, or buoys that have come adrift in harbours. Plastic. A lot of plastic.

He bows his head when he says the word. Then composes himself.

I'm so sorry, I say. I think about saying something else, I'm not sure what. I remember throwing my bank card into the river, just after leaving the house, and feel like crying.

But he's not listening anyway, has his hand up, gently, politely, to silence me, his eyes are fixed on the horizon.

What is it? Can you see one?

Without looking away, he unzips the front pocket of his bag and pulls out a pair of binoculars. The teenagers on the bench stop talking and look up. Something's there. He keeps very still, binoculars over his eyes, I count the seconds.

Nope. Nothing.

Really?

Yes. No. Nothing.

6. The humpback whale

Sometimes, when I feel like it, I show them.

Not now. I'm unseeable. There's pain somewhere. Green blue black where the sun can't get down. The pain is back there, behind me. Maybe it's gone now. I'm watching the tiny grains with their spindly limbs, their tiny, curved mouths. I'm imagining them crawling on my back and I feel sick. There are stories about how those tiny grains ride on the backs of other animals, but I've never seen it. There are stories where they want to haul us out and give us legs. Or they shrink us to be like them. There's nothing up there, just tiny grains and dry dirt. Gasping air and a giant sun that would crack you open. Those tiny grains jostle with the sand and in the air, turning pink in the sky, rolling, rotating, tangled into strings of kelp that become beams of light and an itching noise that is too high and too sharp.

I've been here a long time. I'm old and tired and it hurts. The noise rolls towards me—towards us—through the green blue black. I won't let him see me now. I'm too tired; we're all so tired.

7. Stromness to Kirkwall

The islands rise gently out of the sea, low and long on the horizon. Brownish-green lines at first, coming into focus as we draw nearer. The man on the ferry and I talked some more. He told me his name was Rob, that he lived alone in Kirkwall.

Where are you staying? he asks me as the land rises up on either side of us and the ferry slides into the port.

Oh, um, I hadn't— I don't want to stay with Rob.

There's a youth hostel, he says quickly. *In Kirkwall I mean.*

Great, yes I'll go there.

I can give you a lift if you like.

No, it's OK. I'll probably walk.

He laughs then. *Fine, suit yourself, but it'll take you about four to five hours.*

The ferry jolts into its moorings and the alarms sound for the car passengers. The boat steadies, people gather up bags and coats and stand in anticipation next to the doors.

You really don't want to walk it, honestly. I'll drive you.

Ok, I say, *thanks.*

Seagulls flap lazily across the carpark. Rob leads the way to where he is parked. It's a four-wheel drive; the old-fashioned kind. The paintwork is peeling and the inside smells like diesel. It has a radio that blasts into life when he starts the engine.

Bet you've not been in one of these for a while? he says. *In fact, I bet you're not even old enough to remember when they made cars like this.*

I could tell him that my grandfather used to drive one like this, far away, on a different island, hundreds of miles south of here. But I don't want to get into that. That's how it starts.

No, I say. *Is it very old?*

Oh yes, but it goes just fine for short trips. I just make trips to the beaches, and to the ferry port every few weeks. Daren't take it to the mainland though in case I got stuck there.

I laugh and say something like *if it ain't broke don't fix it*, and then Rob smiles in that large, warm way that he has, and I want to shut my eyes and put my head on the window, but I can't.

The land here isn't like the mainland. The islands over the sea, green and blue and black, side by side. This island lies low to the water, like it's part of the water. I think about the whales. Rob tells me more about his beachcombing. He tells me about posting his finds on the internet.

Stuff washes up here from all over the world. I've found Chinese food packaging before, a lifebelt from a boat that I traced to a port in Barbados. I take pictures and put them on the internet. People get in touch with me to help me identify things. The world is pretty small nowadays.

Yes, it is, I say. *I feel that way more and more.*

It's a strange thing, he says. *You can never really be alone in a world like this. Even up here, everyone's with us.*

The sun is low in the sky when he pulls up outside the youth hostel. *You sure you'll be alright?*

Yes, of course. Thank you. I gather up my bag and my raincoat and open the door.

Hey look, he says as I go to close the passenger door behind me, *there've been sightings on some of the beaches not too far from here. Whales I mean. I'm off over there tomorrow.*

Oh?

Did you want—did you want me to take you?

I remember that I'm there for the whale watching, so I can't really say no.

Sure, yes. Thanks, that would be nice.

8. Scapa

I'm glad you came. It feels right that you're here.

It's dark. There's a breeze, but it's not cold. I have to be back at the youth hostel by 11pm. I've got time. The streets of this town are too narrow and the buildings huddle together. I leave them behind and walk in a straight line. I'm looking for the sea. I follow the beach as it slopes down into the black water. I take off my shoes and leave them on the foreshore. There are no waves, the water holds the islands in their place. It feels warm on my skin. I look down and my feet are like ghosts.

Out here we believe that the land and the sea connect, there's no barrier. Our islands are like sleeping whales on an ocean of time. Some poet said that, and he was almost right. It's different here isn't it? I knew you'd like it. I can feel that you're feeling better. I should tell you though, that my asking you here wasn't all about you. There's all this noise, this poking and bothering in the sand and the soil. It itches. I might have told you that already. They want to know things, but some things are supposed to be unknown.

How are you feeling? I can't keep you here forever. I know that you don't really want to be here.

This was all just rock at one time. Then the rocks became covered in soil and blood and earth. There's richness here. There's gold if you dig down deep enough. Don't tell anyone though. I'm not sure how trustworthy you are, but I feel like you're a good listener.

Perhaps it's time to get out of the water now. Perhaps it's time to sit on the foreshore for a while. There's some whiskey in your bag. Don't worry how it got there. Don't worry. I'm here. There'll be a whale too, I'm sure of it.

9. Skaill

Rob picks me up after lunch.

How was your night?

Ah, fine you know, I say. *Not bad for a single bed in a youth hostel.* I don't tell him about my trip to the beach.

We clatter along deserted roads, winding around farmland and over causeways that span narrow straits. We are almost in the water. I think about my childhood dream, the one where the house is full of water, and we are sea animals, my parents and me. I wonder if the sea ever creeps up over the land here and floods the farms. You don't hear about it, and people have lived here for millennia. We park near some birdwatchers, who are looking out over a wide, white beach, lined with tidemarks of seaweed and shingle.

There's a seal colony over there, look. Rob points to the west, where the birdwatchers have their binoculars trained. I can just make out a grey-brown mass. It feels anticlimactic, my fingers are numb. The wind stings my eyes.

We walk down to the foreshore. There are some dog walkers, more nature-spotters but otherwise it's empty.

We'll walk out to the rocks at the end, see if we can spot something.

We walk side by side. The sand crunches, gently, under our feet.

Have you ever seen a whale before? he asks.

No.

They're amazing creatures, it'll take your breath away.

I'm sure.

*

We reach the rocks and sit down. Rob pulls out his binoculars. The sea warps and swirls, stretching out forever. I realise then, that I'm not at the edge of anything, just a juncture. A ferry crawls across the middle distance.

Where does that one go? I ask.

I think that's the overnight one for Shetland.

What's Shetland like?

Rob's voice is hampered by the wind. My bones feel tired.

Different to here.

Of course. Any whales?

I think so.

Rob takes the binoculars away from his face and turns to me.

Are you—alright?

What? Yes, I mean—of course.

It just seems strange that you'd come all the way here, with hardly any plan. Most people who visit are all bright-eyed and excitable, keen to have 'an experience', they've got all their sights to see, their list to tick off.

I'm sorry. That must get boring.

It's fine, it's alright, we're used to it. It's just strange that you don't seem that way, but you're still a tourist—

I don't really know what I am, or what I'm doing. Sorry.

I wondered, last night after I dropped you off, if you were in some kind of trouble. He looks back out across the bay again. There's a squall in the middle distance, a grey column that blurs the sky and the sea. *I wondered if maybe you were running away from something.*

I look down at my hands. They are bone white.

It's fine, I tell him, *I'm not in any danger.* I'm not sure this is quite true. How can anyone be sure they're not in any danger?

Oh good, he says, his face brightening. *Good. So why here? It's a funny time of year: end of the season, weather's quite changeable. And you don't have a lot of stuff.*

I wonder about telling Rob that I was called here by an assortment of Scottish islands. I wonder about telling him that

I had an epiphany. I want to tell him we've been doing it all wrong, as a species, that the journey is the whole point; keeping going is the point.

I was ill, I say. *I'm better now, but I was ill and stuck indoors for a long time. I needed to move forwards, even if it was slowly.*

Oh right, he says. He looks concerned now. I feel bad for him.

And then I got better and found that I had some time free and I guess—

It felt like a golden opportunity.

Yes.

*

We stay for three hours. Rob has a flask of tea that he shares with me. We talk about the land, but I let Rob's voice wash over me as we both stare at the infinite ocean. My head pounds and I remember that there is half a bottle of whiskey in my bag at the youth hostel. Just after five o-clock he sighs, defeated, and we walk back up the beach together.

I'm sorry I couldn't find one for you, he says as we get back into his car. It's only once we're out of the wind that I realise how cold I was out on the beach.

It's OK, I say. *I really appreciate you taking me. I appreciate you trying.*

He smiles at me and starts the engine.

*

Back in my room at the youth hostel I find the whiskey and retrace my steps from the previous night. I drink from the bottle all the way down to the beach.

10. The Whale Returns

I came all the way here to see you, and you're drunk and asleep. We could have had a conversation.

I can feel you. I heard you. I didn't want to, but I did. I'm not coming any closer. It's not safe. I am not stupid.

I want you to know that we don't have an affinity. I have no secrets to unburden on you. I am simply old and tired.

11. I wake up, still drunk, on the beach

Stones press into my temples. Whalebones. I'm in a church made from whalebone.

My face is resting on the flagstones. Are bones always so cold? My head will hurt too much if I open my eyes. It's nearly light though, I can feel it.

I don't know what I'm supposed to do here. I don't know what any of it means.

The sea rushes up and then hurries away. I roll over and return to sleep.

I'm sorry it didn't work out. You shouldn't have fallen asleep. All you needed to do was put your feet in the water, and the whale would have spoken to you. It can hear you from hundreds of miles away. It can see pretty far too, even in the dark. You probably weren't the right person after all, but I'll be sorry to see you go.

They built this whalebone church here thousands of years ago. See how white it is. So white and so brittle. No one can find it. I will let you see it, but you'll need to leave soon.

Later, the sun tries to pull apart my eyelids. My clothes are damp. I sit up. My mouth is dry. I brought all my stuff with me, didn't I? Yes. I'm still in Kirkwall, aren't I? Yes. I should go home, pack up the sand and the bones and my clothes and travel to the airport and retrace everything, undo everything. But there's a ferry from here on to Shetland. I can go there next. I can walk to the port and wait. It might take an hour and a half. It might take seven hours. I can't remember. It doesn't matter. I have seven hundred pounds in my bag. Or thereabouts. I get it out and count it, then rise to my feet.

Britannia — Azura — Victoria

The beauty of our holidays is that anything goes! Come join us and get into the spirit of relaxation on board one of our majestic five-thousand-passenger ships. Bring as much luggage as you like: your glamorous evening wear, casual attire for relaxing by the pool, and sportswear for those wanting to make use of one of our many fitness facilities. Our stylish robes come in all shapes and sizes.

*

There are seven cruise liners. Until this year, they had been used for round-the-world excursions. Now they are anchored in a bay off the south coast of England. They will be there for the entire summer. The ships can be seen, quite clearly, from cliff paths and beaches along the Jurassic Coast. They are much further away than they appear, and they turn, slowly, on their dynamic anchors, all day and night.

A wild campsite, a working organic farm for most of the year, has just opened for the season. A queue of cars and campervans streams along the coast road, and down the dirt track that leads to the campsite. The cars are parked, and the campers booked in. They can find their own pitches in any of the fields which slope gently towards the cliffs and the paths down to the beach below. There are compostable toilets and solar-powered showers. The sea fills the middle distance, and the campers can hear it wash against the shingle as they put up their tents.

A family of four use homemade bunting to reserve a section of their favourite field. They park their van diagonally across the middle, so that it lets other campers know that they are expecting a big group. Shortly afterwards, their friends drive in with their campervans, put up bell tents and awnings, and soon the area of the field that they have annexed is springing with children and dogs. There is chatter about where the pop-up bar could be, and where they might find the pizza oven, and what time is high tide. The adults in the group marvel that they are outnumbered by their children this year. One child— the eldest child in the party, a teenager, really—carries a notebook. She walks slowly around the tracks at the edges of the campsite, whilst her parents unload their things from their vehicles and greet their friends. She has a notebook and pen; she feels better when she takes notes. As the sun sets, a pale smog rises from the ships, and the sky bruises violently pink. The campsite settles to a hush, the groups hunched around campfires, and the sea waits beneath them.

*

On board, you'll find a fully equipped gym with over three hundred state-of-the-art machines to help maintain even the strictest fitness regimes. Above deck, you can take advantage of our Olympic-sized swimming pool, three tennis courts, all-weather football pitch and croquet lawn, all within easy reach of the central plaza. After your workout, you can enjoy the relaxing and capacious steam room and sauna where you can recharge and unwind.

*

Morning. The eldest child follows her family through the campsite to the cliff path, where they find the little track that leads down to the shingle beach. There are already lots of people down there. The foreshore pitches steeply into the water. There is a pontoon, and small children in neoprene are lining up to jump off it into the waves. The eldest child's mother is worried about her but has put on a bright face. The eldest child's father is carrying a canvas bag full of sun cream, towels, bottles of cider. There are other fathers on the beach too, other mothers, other siblings. The eldest child's small brothers are jangling ahead across the stones, to join their friends. The ships look very close to the land from sea level. The family joins the others.

I can't believe how warm it is this year.

Oh, but it's lovely.

Is this eight years now, or nine?

It's eight, Iris was four the first year—
No, five, darling, five.
Yes, that's right.

The eldest child walks a little way back from the group. The adults have opened their drinks. This is a holiday for everyone, after a difficult year. *Such a strange year! What a year!* the adults say, *and it's only halfway through!* The eldest child remembers when they came the previous year, and there were no cruise ships. There were other things that year though. A dusk walk on the beach, one of the adults— taking one for the team who were back at the campsite opening boxes of wine—leading all the children to a place where they'd seen a seal. There was no seal, but in the dark on the way back, the eldest child noticed a cormorant, dead and greasy—its wings forming an awkward heart-shape— slumped on the steep bank that formed the base of the cliff. No one else saw it.

*

Our luxury spa offers a range of top-of-the-range treatments, from massages to full-body mud masques, from cellulite elimination to crystal healing. We have Swedish masseurs, aestheticians, brow and lash technicians, nail artists and hair stylists on board, as part of our dedicated, 800-strong crew. We have everything you'll need to prepare you for the ritual. Our rituals are 100% traditional using authentic instruments and organic products. Although it's not just relaxation we have to offer! Our ship boasts seventeen evening venues, more than any other vessel of its kind. Our night-time entertainment schedule comprises the very best tribute acts, honouring well-loved bands and singers from every decade. Year on year, our guests are surprised and delighted to be immersed in music from all eras, from the groovy sights and eclectic sounds of the sixties to the latest tween sensation!

*

At lunchtime, some of the group get into the water, warm and petrol blue. The sun lurks behind by a thin veil of cloud; the sky feels heavy.

What are those cruise liners doing there?

No idea, I think some sort of scheme—

No, it's a party! Some exclusive party!

What's what's what's a liner, mummy?

I've been doing a lot of wild swimming recently.

We have too, isn't it lovely.

When did it start being called wild swimming anyway?

Wild wild wild—rahhhh!

Boys—

Boys, not too far out?

Some people have brought disposable barbecues down onto the beach and are cooking lunch. Others have pizza from the woodfired oven at the campsite. Everyone is having a nice time. There are people on paddle boards that inflate automatically when taken out of their carry cases. There are others, on inflatable kayaks in the middle distance. Some are quite far out, and the eldest child wonders if they might make it to the ships. They look like insects, flickering on the oily surface of the ocean.

*

Art lovers, why not take a stroll around one of our seven galleries, or allow yourself to drift away into one of our immersive installations. There's something for everyone. For children, there are focused learning, enrichment and creative programmes, compatible with every sort of operating system. Kids are kept safe and content by our dedicated team of on-site supervisors, and prepared for the ritual by specially-trained professionals. We have an impeccable safety record.

*

Late afternoon. The website for the local newspaper says that no one knows how long the ships will be moored there. People argue in the comments section about the level of pollution that the ships are causing. One says that when they look out at the ships it makes them proud of our country. Most of these cruise ships were built in Italy. There is some speculation about who is on board. The tickets were incredibly expensive, and there were all these checks, lots, and lots of checks. The consensus, in the comments section, between @ProudDad79, @MissMilsy and many others is that people get onto the ships by invite only, and that they are much, much further out to sea than they appear from the land. There is a disagreement, that spirals into insults, about whether the ships hold military personnel, government officials, celebrities, or a secret group comprising all three. At 3:37pm, the moderator turns off the comments.

The families on the beach don't look at the local news, and instead are feeling warm and fuzzy; drunk on sunshine, and wine from a box. It's so normal. *It all feels so normal!* they say. The eldest child takes her brothers and some of the other children into the water. The parents chat on the shoreline about work and the merits of comprehensive education and loft conversions and which kitchen they might choose once the builders can get back in, and how they managed to get along with each other whilst stuck inside that whole time, and how normal—*just how normal! How lovely!*—this all feels. One of the smaller children has caught a jellyfish in a bucket. It hangs, sagging slightly, in the green plastic, like a streak of spilled milk.

*

All of our vessels are hand-built, using traditional ship-building techniques used by our forefathers for centuries. Everything is perfectly safe. We are proud to offer a range of different fine dining and casual eating experiences! An ever-changing array of cuisines and flavours to ignite even the most jaded palette! If you prefer to eat in complete silence, our operatives can bring all of your meals to your cabin. If you need an operative to attend to your cabin and wash and dress you, our teams are only too happy to oblige. We provide a refreshingly intensive teeth-cleaning service at no extra cost. All of our linen is 300 count organically-grown cotton. We absolutely guarantee a good night's sleep, night after night. If you prefer to stay awake for the duration of your stay, however, we operate an hourly alarm service.

*

Evening. The sun sets, and the campsite settles to a murmuring quiet as the younger children are put to bed. The adults and the older children gather around the fire. The moon rises, full and huge like an orange lantern, too big and too close to the land. The eldest child watches as it slides slowly upwards. The adults stop their campfire conversation and gaze up at it with her.

Someone's teenage son, who has been studying astronomy at school, saunters back from the beach, and starts to tell everyone why the moon appears to be different colours on certain nights and random times of the year. He talks about the colours of the moon being a result of the angle of its rising opposite to the angle of the sunset, and the way that the sunlight refracts through the earth's atmosphere. The eldest child listens, as the adults talk over him, convinced that the orange tinge across the moon was in fact to do with the fumes left by the cruise ships.

The teenage astronomer gets bored and starts to walk away, but the eldest child gets up, with her notebook, and follows him. He doesn't mind, he was the eldest child once, before he was the eldest teenager.

That one, he says, *up there, is Betelgeuse.*

The eldest child writes it down.

It's in a constellation called Ursa Major, and it's very old.

He points his bespectacled face up to the sky. The eldest child does the same. She can't really see the star he's pointing to, but she looks anyway. There's a plane flashing quietly amongst the spray of white stars. A plane moving, seven cruise ships swaying in the ocean. It makes her feel dizzy.

It will turn into a supernova one day, says the teenage astronomer, *and the supernova will light up the sky so brightly that it will look—for a long time, like about fifteen minutes or something!—as though our sky has a second sun.*

The eldest child's neck is sore from staring up into the night. She looks out at the cruise ships sitting there in the dark water, their tiny windows glittering, and imagines them suddenly illuminated by a dying star.

Is there anything we can do to stop it? she asks.

Oh no, he says, *it could happen any second. And besides, if it happened now, that would mean Betelgeuse had already died, thousands of years ago, and it was already too late.*

*

Our pools are all heated to a balmy 38 degrees centigrade, the perfect level to prepare you for a day of relaxation and entertainment. We also have monastic ice baths, seclusion chambers and isolation tanks for those who need to get away from it all. We end all of our excursions with a spectacular fireworks display. Survivors are invited to gather on deck and marvel at the artistry of our world-class pyrotechnicians. The explosives are made in the traditional way and kept according to the latest safety legislation. Everything is perfectly safe.

*

Just before midnight. The eldest child gets out of her tent and puts on her shoes. No one sees. She walks purposefully away from the laughter of her parents and their friends around the campfire, picking up a large rubber case that contains a self-inflating kayak. The moon hangs, limpid, above her. On the shore, the kayak unrolls like a tongue and inflates at the push of a button, exhaling into itself, now a solid three-dimensional object. The eldest child drags it into the water. The ships are covered with glittering light, a strange sound pulsates through the water towards her. She tries to count the number of illuminated windows as she pushes with the paddle and the kayak slides away from the shore, but there are too many. They blur into one.

The Unreliable Nature Writer's Taxi Pulls Up Outside, And She Walks Over To It And Opens The Door

– Wait, are you going?

Yeah, my taxi's about to arrive. I'm tired.

– I'll wait with you. You look cold, would you like—

No, that's OK, you don't have to—

– I wanted to say something, about what we were talking about earlier, you've made me think about some things more clearly, but other things feel quite confusing now. Maybe it's those drinks, I don't know—

My taxi's two minutes away. What are you doing—?

– Look, I just need to say something to you.

I've got to leave—why are you—why are you taking your shoes off?

– Look, just wait. I'll pay for your taxi. I just need to say—I mean I just need to tell you this one thing.

OK, fine, but just—could you just put your shoes back on? It's freezing out here—

– What? Oh, no. No, I'm fine. Too hot. That fountain looks lovely and cool, doesn't it? Look, I don't know, I think you're right on a lot of things, but also, kind of *wrong* too? Sorry. I don't think beauty is meaningless, for a start, and I don't think you feel that way either.

OK. Is that it? I have to go. Please, just don't take off your trousers too, what are you doing? Is that blood? I think your hand's really bleeding again—

– But you can't—wait—can't I just—no, driver, just wait, she needs to—

You're standing much too close to me and I really think you need to go and see someone about your hand.

– You're not really free either, you know.

Ok. Goodbye. I'm getting into the taxi. Please go inside, look, the bar staff are coming over.

– Are they? Oh they don't mind. They love me! OK, look, go if you must, but you have to admit it first.

Admit what? Please let go of my coat.

– Admit that you're not free either.

Listen. Everything is going to work out fine for you. I'm sure if you decided to run away to the Scottish Highlands, you'd be welcomed by the residents there with open arms. Now *please* go inside and put some clothes on. Look, this nice man has a first aid kit for you.

– But I need to ask you—

Don't worry, you just need to go back inside. You'll be OK. You'll figure it out.

– …

Go on, off you go. There's your wife now, look?

– I'm sorry. I don't know what I'm doing.

I know. Go inside.

– I'm sorry.

Come and Pick Me Up Immediately

Can you call me? There's something urgent I need.

I know it's Saturday.

I need you.

I NEED TO GET OUT OF HERE.

CALL ME.

I NEED YOU TO TAKE ME TO A WOODLAND STREAM.

Six messages. I read them as I'm getting out of the shower, while my shoulders are still wet. You need me. You wrote it, right there. Those are your words. You know I've seen them, you're typing again, but before you finish, I reply with: *Hi, no problem. I'll leave soon.*

I don't know how to dress, so I put on my work clothes from yesterday. Fresh underwear and tights though, just in case. The skirt already feels too tight. It's hot, even at this time of day. I open the window—filthy again, even though I cleaned it before I showered—and the grey noise of the city seeps in. The roar of traffic jitters through the dust. I would do anything for you. You know that. I need the insurance.

You're where you said you'd be: on the corner, by the church. I see you—flattened against the brick wall in the sunlight—before you see me. Your shirt wrinkles where it tucks into your trousers. I pull up and you wrench open the door, hurl yourself in.

Christ, you took your time, you say. *You alright? You're sweating. You should turn up the cold air in here.*

Am I? I say, *I think I was just in a hurry.*

You have a perfectly symmetrical face. It's like they made you in a factory. Why do conventionally attractive men look disturbing up close?

You're talking now: *That was bloody awful, can't believe I agreed to go* (you pat your chest) s*hit—fuck—my wallet. We'll have to—no. Can't go back in. Not now. Have you got the directions I sent? Never mind, it's on my phone.*

You lean over, slide your phone into the holder in front of the steering wheel. You smell amazing. You've been drinking. There's a stain on your tie. Blood, or red wine. We drive out of the city with the sky thick and beige above our heads. You open all the windows and stick your hand out, letting the air stream through your fingers. The buildings rise on either side in the heat. Dust fills the car.

Over and over again, you say: *I want to be in the forest.*

We drive for an hour. The city ebbing away slowly behind us. The air is clearer out here, the visibility improves the further we drive, but the land is a sick, burnt ochre. I wonder if this forest is real at all, but then it appears, a green smudge on the horizon. There's a carpark, neat and gravelled; signs point to different paths here and there. We park. You look at me as if I'm supposed to know what to do next. I can't ever know what to do when I'm this close to you.

Let's walk, you say.

Really?

Yes. Come on, chop-chop.

No—I don't think it's a good idea. It's nearly midday.

So?

So—we're not supposed to be out in this heat.

You throw your head back and laugh. Then, you judder at the door handle—twice—before lurching out onto the gravel.

It'll be cooler under the trees, you say. I need to do something to slow you down.

It's funny how everyone follows the path. You're slurring your words now; still drunk. *What if we just run off to the left now, just here? Who would do anything?*

You stagger into the woodland, your words spilling out behind you into the heavy air: *What if we just started going this way? Would anyone stop us? Who the fuck could stop me anyway? Are you listening? Shit. My wallet. Never mind.*

I follow, trying to survey the woodland at the same time. You carry on at a haphazard trot, still talking; yelling, in fact.

This isn't the wild. It's managed by the estate. Managed wilderness. What do they mean 'managed' anyway? Do they

know all the animals that are here? Do they know what they're
up to all the time? You can't have cameras everywhere!

You're not waiting to see if I have any replies. Instead,
you're taking off your shoes and socks; placing them neatly
on a tree stump. A woman runs past in a full reflective veil,
gloves, dark glasses. It must cost a fortune; she's probably a
semi-professional trail-runner. She glances over but—seeing
me look back at her—pretends to check her wristband. She
speeds up, disappearing into the cavernous shade.

You're off again too, running on the balls of your feet,
picking your way across the forest floor. I think about
gathering up your shoes and following with them, but I then
remember that I'm not your mother, or your wife. I look at the
shoes—wondering what it is that I think I am—and decide
to leave them there. The brown leather glistens against the
dull edge of the tree trunk; your socks spill out from within.

When I catch up to you, you're leaning forwards against a
tree with your hands pressed up against the bark, head bent
as though counting in a game of hide and seek. You're not
out of breath, but you've loosened your tie. Why are you
wearing a suit anyway? It's the weekend. Were you at a
funeral? Oh god, were you at a wedding? Whose wedding?
Whose wedding were you at? I almost ask, but you turn
to face me with one hand still pressed against the tree (so
handsome, even in this state) and smile. You take my hand—
it feels dry around mine—and set off again.

Why is it that men like you move through the countryside as if you own the place? Is it some sort of inherited entitlement? I feel awkward everywhere I go. Or perhaps it's just bravado: you think that walking with purpose will make everything fine.

You let go of my hand—at once a disappointment and a relief—and I run along behind you.

There's water around here. I can feel it, you shout.

You're following the land as it slopes away downhill. You're still running, jogging really, with leaf-litter stuck to your feet. I can hear something. There *is* a stream; you were right. Now you're running even faster, taking off your jacket as you run, pausing to drape it over a branch before you take off again. The jacket lingers for a moment before slithering onto the earth below.

You don't stop or even look back; you're unbuttoning your shirt. I gather up your jacket; it smells like you. I try to stop smelling it, but I can't. The woodland air intensifies the notes in the perfume. Or perhaps it's the woodland that smells like this. No. Vetiver doesn't grow here. They've tried but it's not possible, even in poly-tunnels. Sandalwood doesn't grow here either. How many men smell the same as you—as this jacket—right now? I close my eyes for a moment and let things go dark. I refuse to be drawn into this. I won't be drawn in. I said it to myself in the quietest voice as I drove you here, while you were shouting and laughing and crying in the passenger seat.

You're further up ahead now, jogging through the trees, skipping over roots and fallen branches, bobbing in and out of the pools of sunlight, shirt flapping behind you. Your feet go brush-brush-brush on the forest floor. Behind us and ahead of us: trees. A squirrel that was, a moment ago, part of a tree trunk weaves its way upward as we hurry past. I keep reminding myself. This isn't a real forest. There's no way you can get lost if it's not a real forest. Someone will always rescue you. You're still going, still jogging, dodging tree stumps and logs like this is a computer game. I'm out of breath and it's much too hot.

My mother used to say, *at this time of year, the sun is as strong in Britain as it is in the Mediterranean*. A memory glistens. Chalky sunblock rubbed on too hard. It had to go everywhere: ears, feet, nose. *When you're a grown-up you can use tanning oil*. The tanning oil was in a brown bottle with an orange palm tree and a yellow setting sun. Palm trees were never orange unless they were on fire. I got burned by the sun when I was a child. It only happened once, but that was enough to put me at risk. Later, I watched in the bathroom mirror at the skin that was stripped from my arms and legs like papery tree bark.

You're stopping. A heart-shaped patch of sweat bleeds across your back and your shirt is stuck to the skin underneath. There's a flash of blood across your left heel. You have ripped your trousers, but you haven't noticed.

I'm sorry. I shouldn't have done this. Your chest rises and falls. *We shouldn't have come here.*

I'm a bit worried about your wallet, I say.

Oh, shit. Yes. We should find it. There's something in there for you. You pat yourself down again, even though you can see me holding your jacket.

Maybe it's here somewhere, you say, pointing further into the trees. You take off again, faster this time. I can see the stream hurtling across the forest floor. The sun is much too hot. My brain is poaching. I'm going to burn. No. I take my tablets.

You slow to a walk, start taking off your shirt. You can't see me looking at you. You look how I imagined you would. This isn't what I wanted though; this isn't how I wanted it to be. It's too bright. This is too much. I wonder if I could unlock your phone and call someone. I try to fish it out of your jacket pocket, but it thuds softly on the earth. There's no signal out here. It's one of the few places left around here with no signal. You'd said all this in the car, but I had pretended not to hear. *How could you possibly know?* I had thought.

You turn to me then: *I'm sorry for all this. I really am. I know this is far above your paygrade, and you don't deserve this, but really, you're the only one I can trust.*

I'm probably blushing, but the sun is so hot out here it would be impossible to notice. The skin on your chest is intensely pink.

Have I ruined your weekend?

No, it's OK. I don't mind.

You must have had things you needed to do.

No, no. It's fine. Really. (What I don't say is, *I have no weekend. I have nothing to do, besides this*). *I'm a bit worried about your wallet. And about being out in the sun like this.*

Oh god don't worry; you've had the jabs, right? The premium plan's quite good because you—

And then you fall silent. Because there, on the other side of the stream is an animal. It's a deer; a stag. Obviously it's a stag. It's always a stag in stories like this. You take my hand again. It's a real handhold now, not like earlier. I wonder if you know you're doing it. I feel sick. Your fingers interlace with mine, gently. Your thumb—your left thumb—is on top of my right thumb. My whole arm is on fire. My head is on fire. Your chest rises and falls. The stag is motionless and much too big, far bigger than I could have imagined, standing side-on. Perfectly rendered. Quiet.

We stay very still, your hand still curled around mine. I don't want to move my fingers in case you let go. The stag dips his head—slowly—towards the stream. His black eyes mirror the forest as his mouth meets with the water.

See, this is why I wanted to come here. For something like this. A real thing; a real experience. Well. Real-ish.

But when you say the words, even so very close to my ear like that, the miniscule gesture of your lips causes the stag to quiver; his muscles tense and ripple and he springs away. Gone. Your hand, at the same time, releases its grip on mine. We watch as the stag fades back into the forest.

Your hands are on my shoulders, your face is very close.

It's time, you say.

I close my eyes, ready. This is it. This is really happening. Here in the woods; just the two of us. But you stagger backwards, laughing, and then you're running towards the stream. It's barely deep enough to cover your ankles but you splash into the water anyway—whooping—and then tumble down into it.

*

When it was all over, you stood up and gathered up your clothes. I followed as you ambled back to the carpark like there was all the time in the world. Your face was turned to the sky—palms facing outwards—like a saint. The midday heat had eased by then, and more people were out on the designated paths in veils or carrying parasols. You stopped briefly, to put your trousers back on, and your shirt, which you left unbuttoned. Your hair was still wet and tousled from the stream. A couple with a baby in a shrouded pushchair crossed our path. They glanced at us before looking away.

We walked straight past the tree stump with your shoes and socks. I looked over my shoulder at them—almost invisible now against the darkening forest—as we carried on. You didn't break your stride.

When we arrived back at the carpark the sun had dipped below the tree line, casting languid shadows across the cars.

You said: *thank you for this. I know how hard you work. I know how hard this job can be.*

It's OK, I said.

I want you to know I appreciate you. I want you to be happy in your work. There was a rift in your voice, a crack.

It's OK, I said.

There was the same ice-cream dispenser in the carpark from earlier. It was driverless, and looked like a giant silver lozenge. We went over and I ran my hand along its cool surface, touching the reflection of our faces, with the trees and the sky behind them. We looked good together. But perhaps you'd look good with anyone. I caught you watching me, and for a moment I thought you might say something else, but instead you pulled your wallet from your trouser pocket. As you drew a card to tap the ice-cream dispenser a series of printed photographs—photographs of you as a boy—fluttered onto the gravel below. You didn't notice when I crouched down to pick them up.

Creativity Enlightenment:
Day Three

Someone has stolen our muse. We heard a strange noise and woke up, all of us at once. Then we came downstairs and found that the back door was open and banging in the breeze. Then we went upstairs and found that he wasn't in his bed.

We checked all over the house. He wasn't in the kitchen or the dining hall or in anyone's room. He wasn't in the print room, or any of the studios, or the music room, or the library. He wasn't in the store cupboard. He wasn't at his charging point. He wasn't at any of the other charging points. We sent a message to the host, but the host was out of reach.

We went out—all eight of us, the whole group!—in our bare feet, into the rose garden. We walked around the grounds in our dressing gowns, and we checked in the orchard and the bushes by the pond. We took our binoculars and looked out over the fields, which was when we came to realise that he's gone.

He's gone.

Is he?

Yes!

What was that?

He's gone—

I can't believe someone would break in here and take him.

He hasn't been taken. He's left of his own accord.

Why would he want to leave? He's supposed to stay here all the time, I thought. He wouldn't want to leave. He's not *supposed* to want to leave.

I'm so frustrated. I was due to spend some time with him this morning. We were going to take a walk along the river.

I did that with him yesterday, it was magical. We talked about the Romantic poets. The way the light on the water reflected onto his face was just incredible. I came back and wrote for hours.

God, that sounds amazing. I'm jealous.

Me too. I know that's probably not the done thing—you know—to admit that you're jealous. But I am.

It's a horrible feeling, isn't it?

Horrible, yes.

Horrible.

I miss him already.

I miss him too.

I feel terrible; like everything is ebbing out of me.

We may as well give up. How are we supposed to work now?

It hurts.

I agree, it hurts. It's like I have an actual, physical injury. I know that sounds crazy, but I'm in pain.

They should have done something to stop him from leaving.

I wouldn't have applied to come here if it hadn't been for their muse.

Me too. I wanted to attend a programme with its own muse. I did a lot of research. I was *so* looking forward to the use of this muse.

Oh, I wasn't bothered, but then I saw him, and had that time with him and—well—you all know what I'm getting at.

I actually only came for the woodland, and the quiet. But the muse was a big part of it; a nice bonus.

What are we supposed to do out here now? I feel adrift without him.

We're going to need inspiration. We're going to need that feeling he gives us. Is there some other muse on one of the other sites do you think? Maybe they'll bring one in?

Oh yes! Maybe there's a back-up muse.

They really should have a back-up muse.

Oh well, I think it's incredible that they've got one at all, especially one like him. He's amazing.

Yes, and no one would keep a back-up muse; it's just unheard of. Too costly. Having one like this is such a privilege.

Well, it was until he went missing.

I felt like we had a connection.

Yes, me too. The other day, when we were sitting down by the pond, he came very close to me. He put his arm across my shoulder, and I put my head on his chest. He said something about my work which had never occurred to me before. He stroked my hair. There was a feeling, like he truly understood me. I think he truly understood my work; what I was trying to do.

Yes, that happened with me too. He did that with me too. He pointed out lots of things in my work that I hadn't seen yet.

He was so insightful about my work too; he spoke for ages about connection and meaning and intimacy. It was enlightening.

I know that's all part of the process, but I really did feel something. My paintings are luminous when he's in them; they come alive. He's changed my work forever.

Why didn't we lock the door?

Who was last to come in from the garden yesterday evening?

It doesn't matter. We need to go out and look for him. He can't have gone outside the grounds. This type of muse shouldn't really go further than that. There's the main road but it's miles to get up there. No one will have mistaken him for—

That's right. He's obviously not a hitchhiker or a game keeper or anything. He'll be clearly identifiable as the muse from this place. Any decent person would just pick him up and return him.

I miss him. God. I really miss him.

I feel awful.

I feel like I don't know what's real anymore. I feel like he's betrayed us. I know that's ridiculous. I know, I know.

Yes, but our feelings are still valid. The feelings we had, that we *still have*, are real.

I feel like everything I've made since we came here has been a lie. What good is it now that he's gone?

Wasn't it always a lie?

Please, no. That's not helpful.

I'm going to burn it all. All of my paintings, and my prints and sketches.

I'm going to burn my notebooks.

I'm going to take my violin and all of my sheet music into the woods and smash them down into that ravine near that badger's set. Come on, let's go. I can't stand this anymore.

How could he do this to us?

I almost feel like he didn't love us.

Well, he's not really *meant* to love us.

Yes of course, but he's supposed to *act* like he does. I was enjoying *feeling* like he loved me.

I didn't get that much from him, if I'm honest.

I felt like he was looking over my shoulder a lot of the time. Also, some of the things he said felt a bit—I don't know—rehearsed, perhaps?

Oh, I didn't find that at all. I felt like it was all genuine with me. I felt like we really had something. I've made some of my best work in the last few days.

I've never felt so productive.

I have been to places where the muse was a lot better; a lot more engaged. Maybe he was new. Maybe there's more work that needs to be done on him.

I'm devastated. This is heart-breaking. He has broken my heart.

I want my money back.

It's not just about the money. It's about our time. It's about our work. It's about us investing in this residency and this place and this muse, and then him—them, I mean—letting us down.

We should still ask for a refund...or at least a part-refund.

We're bereft. We don't know what to do.

I feel like I'm floating; like nothing has meaning anymore.

I feel like I could just drift off on the air, like a spore.

I feel like I could wash into the stream and let the current take me.

I feel so small; like I'm being carried out to sea where I'll live suspended in the current until the dark mouth of a whale closes around me.

That's a bit melodramatic. I don't think it's that bad.

I do.

We do. His behaviour is unacceptable. This situation is unacceptable.

Come to think of it. I'm starting to realise that maybe he wasn't all that useful after all.

What do you mean?

I mean, he's not really here, even when he *is* here, is he?

No, no, I can't—

Look. You've said it yourself—and you too, a few of you actually—that some of his lines sounded rehearsed.

That's true...

Yes.

But, but, but that's not the *point*.

What is the point then?

The point is that *he* makes *us* feel things. *He* inspires *us*.

Yes, but in order to feel the things, we need a degree of cognitive dissonance that I think is too much of a stretch for a group as collectively intelligent—as bright minded—as ourselves.

So, what you're saying, is that—

Yes. This muse was never powerful enough to cope. It's not our fault. We are just very very advanced, it would seem. Very creative. Too creative for this muse. We've broken him essentially.

I told you we should have booked the premium package.

I think it's just a case of us having evolved beyond the offer of this muse.

This is ridiculous. He's not broken, he's just gone. We just need to make a complaint to the host, that's all.

Ah—do you think they took him away in the night maybe, maybe they'll bring a better one?

Oh for goodness' sake they *don't do that*.

Please, all of you. This is very upsetting. Some of us are still very upset. Some of us felt things, some of us loved him.

Please, please stop.

We are very upset, that much is agreed. What can we do about it? Is there a phone number we can—

There's a number in the handbook. I'll go and get it.

Oh, look there's a section in there. 'Muse', see?

What does it say?

It says that this type of muse is able to leave the premises.

Oh, for god's sake.

Yes, look here it says that every third day he takes himself off into the forest where there's a stream.

Ah yes of course, there's that recharging thing they do nowadays—

No, it's not actually a recharging thing, it's more like an update or something? A refresh.

It says that he leaves 'in the early hours of the morning, goes to the stream and then returns, refreshed and re-energised, just after the residents have eaten breakfast.'

Oh yes, breakfast! I'm starving actually.

It's nearly time, isn't it? Shall we—

There he is!

Where?

There! Just coming back now through the trees. Oh, thank God for that.

I'm *so* relieved.

Look, he's dripping wet.

He's so handsome.

Is it me, or does he seem to have become *more* handsome?

He looks better than ever.

Honestly.

Do we need to wait for him here, do you think, or shall we go and eat?

I think he's alright to let himself in, don't you?

Oh, we are *just so* relieved.

He came back for us. He *does* want to be here. He *does* want to be with us.

We're so happy.

So happy, yes. He does care.

He does. Everything's alright.

Acknowledgements

This collection is dedicated to Clementine and Lilah. My infinite thanks to them, and all of these...

My brilliant family: Bryan and Christine Carroll. Henry and Em. Mr and Mrs AGW Clarke. Katherine Clarke. All other Carroll and Clarke affiliates.

All the friends who have read my stories, come to readings and generally tolerated my being absent for large chunks of life while I write.

My industrious agent Ludo Cinelli. My visionary editor Tom Conaghan.

Versions of some of these stories have appeared in various publications. My thanks to editors at *The White Review*, *The London Magazine*, *Gutter*, *Short Fiction Journal*, *The Lonely Crowd*, and, especially, the tenacious Gary and Hannah at *Lunate Journal*.

My tutors and academic mentors at Bath Spa and Exeter Universities, in particular, Richard Kerridge for his invaluable guidance.

AHM and JJ for your meticulous editorial support and unwavering friendship. GG for your powerful brain and dark heart. I am wildly lucky to have found you all.